KEEPING RABBITS

KEEPING RABBITS
A COMPLETE MANUAL

Brian Leverett

BLANDFORD PRESS
London · New York · Sydney

First published in the UK 1987 by Blandford Press
Artillery House, Artillery Row, London SW1P 1RT

Copyright © 1987 Brian Leverett

Distributed in the United States by
Sterling Publishing Co, Inc,
2 Park Avenue, New York, NY 10016

Distributed in Australia by
Capricorn Link (Australia) Pty Ltd
PO Box 665, Lane Cove, NSW 2066

British Library Cataloguing in Publication Data

Leverett, Brian
  Keeping rabbits : a complete manual.
  1. Rabbits
  I. Title
  636'.9322   SF453

ISBN 0 7137 1864 1

Typeset by Poole Typesetting (Wessex) Limited, Bournemouth.
Printed in Great Britain by Biddles Ltd., Guildford

CONTENTS

ACKNOWLEDGEMENTS

I should like to acknowledge the help provided by the following bodies and individuals, without whose co-operation and assistance this book would not have been possible:

The British Rabbit Council;

The directors of the American Rabbit Breeders Association and the Rabbit Council of New Zealand, particularly Mr S. Baldwin, for providing information on the Fancy in their particular countries and allowing me to use same.

I should also like to express a debt of gratitude to those fanciers who allowed their rabbits to be photographed and who have talked to me about rabbits over several years, especially Mr B. Hawkins of Poole, Dorset.

I am particularly grateful to Dr T. Reed, President of the ARBA for allowing me to reproduce the chapter on ailments and diseases from *A Progressive Program for Raising Better Rabbits and Cavies*, and for his encouragement for the book from its inception, and Mr R.J. Newman M.Sc. for the painstaking efforts he put in to obtain the majority of the photographs.

I am also grateful to Mr S. Allen, international gold medallist chef, for help with producing photographs relating to dressing carcasses and information on the culinary uses of rabbits.

I should also like to thank Hannafords for permission to reproduce the photographs on pp 15 and 16.

THE HISTORY AND ORIGINS OF THE DOMESTIC RABBIT

THE WILD RABBIT

The domestic rabbit in all of its many varieties of size, shape, colour, markings and fur types is derived from one species, the wild rabbit (*Oryctolagus cuniculus*), for, although there are twenty-five varieties of wild rabbit throughout the world, Man has only tamed and bred one.

The wild rabbit has brown-grey or Agouti markings and its fur helps to provide camouflage and maintain the body temperature at 36°C. As the rabbit is prey to many carnivores, its eyes are set on both sides of its head to give the maximum angle of vision; these eyes have movable lower lids which, like the upper lids, are equipped with eyelashes. A movable eye-covering (the nictitating membrane) travels from the inner corner to clean the eye. The smellers, the strong long hairs to the side of the nose, are sense organs of great importance in the burrow, but are of no importance in the tame rabbit, being almost non-existent in the Rex mutation. This is one of the reasons why this particular variation, so popular with the exhibitor, has not managed to survive in the wild. However, there are probably more important reasons, such as the short coat of the Rex being unable to provide the animal with the necessary heat insulation to withstand the very wide temperature range in its environment.

THE DOMESTIC RABBIT

The skeletons of the giant breeds and dwarf varieties show an increase and decrease in size respectively when compared with the skeleton of the wild rabbit and, in the Belgian Hare shape and the mandolin type the curvature of the spine has been increased. All breeds, however, possess the same basic skeleton (Fig. 1) as their wild ancestors — a skeleton characteristic of powerful running animals which could escape from their pursuers. Such a defence mechanism is not needed by hutch animals and the greater range of skeletal shape possible, together with the variation in the colour and markings of the fur, as well as its texture and length, has led to the many variations of the basic type.

The wild rabbit is essentially a social animal, i.e. each member has a well-established position in the pecking order. In the hutch animal, living an independent existence, this social order is missing, but it is possible to observe aspects of social behaviour, such as young rabbits cleaning each other and bucks 'chinning' their cage, i.e. marking out their territory with

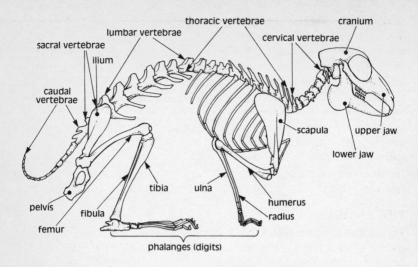

Fig. 1. The skeleton of the rabbit.

strong-smelling substances secreted by their scent glands. The stamping of feet following a sudden noise is another form of instinctive behaviour designed to warn the warren of imminent danger.

All breeds of rabbits possess the basic skeleton and even breeds as different as the Belgian Hare, the New Zealand White and the Netherlands Dwarf all have the same number of vertebrae. Individual bones may differ in relative size, but it is the muscle attachment and the curvature of the spine that collectively have a far more pronounced effect upon the shape. The conformation of the domestic rabbit is the result of the adaption of the skeleton of its wild ancestor and a poor skeletal structure results in bad type. Many faults are a direct consequence of faults in the skeleton. If the lower jaw protrudes beyond the upper jaw the animal is undershot, if it does not reach the upper jaw the animal is overshot. Where the radius and ulna bend outwards, the rabbit is bow-legged, possibly as a result of rickets caused by poor nutrition. Where the two knee joints move in towards each other, throwing the back feet outwards, the animal is referred to as being cow-hocked.

THE RABBIT IN PRE-HISTORY

Prior to the Roman civilisation there is very little recorded history of the rabbit, although by 10,000 BC man knew how to make nets and hunt with bows and arrows. In both hunter-gatherer and emerging urban societies the value of this readily regenerated food supply would soon have become apparent. The rabbit originated around the Mediterranean, probably on, or

8

close to, the Iberian peninsula. As the Mediterranean civilisations flourished and colonised the rest of the known world, it is reasonable to assume that they took this valuable; and undemanding food source with them. The Romans were almost certainly responsible for introducing the rabbit into France, but they do not appear to have taken the animal across the Channel. The rabbit seems to have been introduced to the British Isles by the Normans almost immediately after the Conquest, a view supported by the total lack of early archaeological evidence and the absence of any mention of the animal in the *Domesday Book*, a work noted for its meticulous atttention to detail. Once the Normans did arrive they appear, from contemporary accounts, to have lost very little time in establishing the rabbit in Britain.

THE RABBIT IN THE UK

The advantage of the rabbit to mediaeval society was that it could live on very poor pasture. It was one of the very few sources of fresh meat available during the winter months at a time when all but breeding stock of the largest animals were slaughtered during the autumn, due to the lack of winter fodder.

There appear to have been three methods of keeping rabbits. The simplest was to release them onto an island and, once they were established, to hunt them. Such a method required little labour other than destroying the animals' natural predators. On some islands where this has happened, the melanistic (black) rabbit has become the dominant form. The disadvantage of such a method of husbandry was its restriction to a small area off the coast. Far more widespread was the system of establishing warrens or enclosures. Due to the rabbit's ability to burrow, it would not have been long before some escaped to establish truly wild populations; and thus the colonisation of the whole mainland began, a process which, surprisingly, was not completed until towards the end of the nineteenth century. Once established, the rabbit became the widest-spread and economically the most harmful agricultural pest in the country, the reverse of its original role, until the myxomatosis epidemic of 1953. The majority of the feudal barons in the Middle Ages had their own warreners, the modern name Warren being descended from this mediaeval profession. Rabbit meat was undoubtedly a delicacy, appearing in the coronation feast of Henry IV.

The first hutches were probably built in the monasteries, where, as well as being raised for food in the usual way, the newborn or unborn 'feti', which were a delicacy known since Roman times, were classified, together with eggs, as 'not meat' and could be eaten during the Lent period. Along with the new type of farming necessary to harvest the 'feti', would have come the first opportunity for selective breeding. It is almost certain that breeding would have been very close as, once the initial stock had been obtained from the wild, there would have been few opportunities to introduce new blood. Fur would have contributed an important part to the garments of the time and, when a mutation such as the Albino emerged, it would have been prized for the enormous potential of its skin. Over a period of time, strains of white rabbits would have been developed simultaneously in many different places. Other mutations and curiosities would have been prized, possibly as pets for children of the nobility. It is reasonable to assume that, by the end of the Middle Ages, at least some varieties different from the wild Agouti form were known. Nevertheless the evolution of today's many breeds would have been gradual and the multitude of varieties that we now know have only emerged during the last century. Thomas Bewick, in his *History of Quadrupeds* (1792), classifies rabbits as small and large tame, Angoras, Piebald (could this be the first reference to English spotting?) and the hooded rabbit.

The original name of the animal was 'coney' but, during the Middle Ages, the young were increasingly referred to as 'rabbits', and, by about the end of the fifteenth century, this had become the predominant name for the adult. Today the term coney is only used to describe the fur of the animal, but it does survive in English place names, such as Coneygarth and Coney Weston, recording the once great importance of this little mammal.

THE DEVELOPMENT OF THE RABBIT FANCY

The breeding of rabbits holds the same challenge as breeding racehorses or dogs and when, during the eighteenth and nineteenth centuries, the interest in improving the quality of livestock grew and competition between breeders became popular as part of the Industrial Revolution, rabbit-breeding gained a new dimension, that of a sport. During the early days, no one spent money on housing or food for their rabbits, so here was a sport in which the rich held no advantage over the poor and in which success depended on the breeder's skill.

If the rich had no advantage this did not stop them from taking up the challenge and, from the earliest days, the Fancy has had its wealthy benefactors. The Rabbit Fancy is one of the very few activities to hold equal attraction for the rich and not so rich.

As the breeding of rabbits for specific characteristics emerged, the next step was for an agreed standard, a norm against which the rabbits could be judged. Such standards would have varied initially both between different areas and between the clubs which had been established to run the shows which would often be held in a public house. From these humble beginnings, area and national breed clubs emerged, these in turn coming together to form national organisations such as the British Rabbit Council (BRC). Once the Fancy had been placed on a firm footing it went from strength to strength. During the early days, there were people who set out to buy success, spending huge sums on stock. Such investments have seldom been justified, as there seem to be no short cuts, sound breeding methods and good husbandry being the only requirements necessary to win. Disappointed with failure, the cheque-book fanciers soon left and today the sport is still one that calls for only modest financial investment.

Fancy-rabbit-breeding probably reached its zenith immediately prior to and just after World War 2. In a time of economic depression, rabbit meat took on its former role as an important nutritional source. During this time a small stud could be fed on food gathered from the hedgerow and from garden waste, providing virtually free meat for anyone who was prepared to take the trouble to raise the stock. Before the advent of manmade fibres, rabbit skins were in demand. During the 1930s in the UK, a prime Chinchilla skin would sell for 10s (50 n.p.). As this represented one-fifth of a labourer's wages for a week, it is not surprising that rabbits were popular, and with this popularity came a rapid rise in the quality of the animals that were kept.

Myxomatosis was responsible for a sudden drop in the popularity of the flesh of the domestic rabbit as well as that of the wild version. Coupled with this was the decrease in the amount of land available for the gathering of wild food. As a result of urban development and the increased use of weedkillers, rabbit-keeping experienced as drastic a change as it had known at any time in its long history. A commercial rabbit industry emerged, concerned with the greatest return on capital; the animals were kept in cheap wire cages; the maximum number of litters, rather than just one or two quality animals, were sought from the does and consideration was given to nutrition and food conversion rates. The advent of manmade fibres had reduced the demand for furs. The Fancy became almost a pure sport, but it certainly benefited from the research financed by the commercial activity and was quick to grasp the advantages of pellet-feeding. Today both forms of rabbit-keeping happily coexist with the commercial operations representing an important aspect of agriculture and the Fancy still holding the attractions that it always did.

RABBIT-KEEPING IN THE USA

As Europeans colonised the rest of the world, they took with them their domestic animals. The rabbit probably went to North America with the earliest settlers. There are species of rabbit which are indigenous to the New World, but none of these have been used in the breeding of the modern domestic rabbit. Until 1898, when a Belgian Hare boom occurred and it is reported that good examples changed hands for anything from $100 to $200, there appears to have been little tendency to breed fancy rabbits in the USA. The first specialist breed clubs occurred at this time with the first national rabbit association emerging in 1910. The history of domestic rabbit-keeping is well documented from that time by the American Rabbit Breeders Association (ARBA).

RABBIT-KEEPING IN NEW ZEALAND

Rabbit-keeping is a comparatively recent activity in New Zealand, in spite of the fact that one of the major breeds of meat rabbit is named after the country. In 1980, the Government first permitted the importation of six breeds: the Angora, Flemish Giant, Chinchilla, New Zealand White,

Californian and Rex. In addition to these commercial breeds, Dutch, Dwarf, Fox and Tans were allowed into the country in June 1985. The Fancy appears to be making rapid progress and, although it is impossible to draw comparisons with both the UK and the USA, it will be interesting to study the growth in this area as it may shed further light on the development of breeds in an isolated environment, where the origins of the initial stock are fully known. The Fancy is catered for by the Rabbit Council of New Zealand.

RABBIT-KEEPING IN MAINLAND EUROPE

The development of rabbit-keeping in mainland Europe probably followed the same pattern as it did in the UK. Important mutations were first observed on the Continent, such as the three forms of Rexing. It seems likely that Dutch were first bred in the Netherlands and that it was from a group of rabbits imported into Britain that the British Dutch were established. Similarly there would seem to be little doubt that the Rhinelander originated in Germany, but it should not be taken as a general rule that the name of a breed necessarily has any connection with the country from which it derives its names. Japanese and Himalayans, both natural mutations, were almost certainly first observed and bred from in the western hemisphere, and it was the tendency to associate strange and exotic things with the Orient rather than any statement of origin that led to the coining of the names.

Not surprisingly an examination of the breed standards adopted by different countries shows both similarities and differences. Although genetics dictate the main features of the breed, the overall make-up of the ideal animal will depend upon the results of selection for specified features over a number of generations. This allows for several different breed standards to be written. In some cases these are so far removed from each other, as in the case of the French and English Angoras, that two distinctly different breeds, expressing the same main feature, have emerged. When considering any breed it is necessary to base that assessment on the breed standard or standard of perfection of the country concerned. Outcrosses by means of importation may offer a means of improving the rabbits of another country, but unless both standards are similar and, more importantly, are interpreted similarly, such imports will have the reverse of the effect desired.

Today rabbit-keeping is an important part of farming throughout the world and provides a meat which is richer in protein and lower in fat than any other comparable form of animal flesh. Moreover, the ability of the rabbit to eat a variety of foods and to withstand extremes of temperature makes it an ideal potential protein source for emerging nations. Rabbits are also used extensively in laboratory work but, above all, they are perhaps the most popular of children's pets. In addition the Fancy provides thousands of people worldwide with relaxation, sport and not a little academic stimulation.

THE LAW, HOUSING
AND EQUIPMENT

RABBIT-KEEPING AND THE LAW

You do not need planning permission to place a small building or structure on land within your boundary for the purposes of keeping rabbits providing that:

1) the building is for the benefit of the occupants of the house, and this includes buildings to house animals kept for domestic needs or for the personal enjoyment of the occupants of the house;
2) the building is not more than 400 mm (13 ft) in height if it has a ridged roof or 300 mm (3 ft) otherwise;
3) the addition of the building or structure will not result in more than half of the garden of the house being covered by buildings.

In practice, this means that, providing you own a house which has a back garden, you may almost certainly keep rabbits, provided that it is not for business purposes. Should you have any doubts, or wish to engage in a larger-scale operation, then contact your local town-planning officer. Landlord/tenant agreements may preclude the keeping of livestock, and tenants are advised to take advice before purchasing any animals.

This is an interpretation of the relevant laws of the UK. The laws of other countries may differ and readers should seek clarification in their own country.

HOUSING

Rabbits are tolerant of a wide range of temperatures and will survive both tropical conditions and snow and ice, given the right housing. However, it is essential to keep the animals dry at all times. Where the hutches are sited outdoors, they must not be facing the prevailing winds, and, as well as being completely waterproof, should be provided with an awning or covering at night, during storms and when a doe is due to give birth.

INDOOR RABBITRIES

It is more convenient for both the stock and the owner if the animals are kept in an indoor rabbitry. In selecting a shed for a rabbitry, always ensure that it is sufficiently large and that there are preferably two windows which can be opened for ventilation during hot weather. Choose a wooden structure and cover the roof with a waterproof felt. Avoid corrugated iron which retains heat and can produce temperatures sufficiently high to kill the animals during hot spells. One solution is to provide a 'carport'-type structure, consisting of a supported roof, open at the sides. This will protect the hutches from rainfall, will allow easy access for cleaning and cost only a fraction of the price of a totally enclosed building. Open-sided buildings offer many advantages to commercial ventures in tropical regions. Where stock are to be attended after the hours of darkness, it will be necessary to provide some form of lighting, preferably electric.

SINGLE HUTCHES AND UNITS

Where one or two rabbits are being kept solely as pets, the most suitable form of accommodation is the two-compartment hutch (Fig. 2). The enclosed section will provide shelter in times of rain, even if the structure is situated outside. It is also ideal for breeding purposes. It should be realised that any outside hutch must be capable of withstanding continuous rain on occasions, and you should never buy the cheaper hardboard, three-ply or chipboard hutches that are on sale in many pet shops. Even if you can provide adequate shelter they will soon be spoilt by the rabbit's urine, which, as well as staining,will form a heavy white deposit as a result of excreted calcium compounds.

TWO- AND THREE-TIER UNITS

For keeping several rabbits the most effective housing, both in terms of space and cost, are the two- and three-tier systems in which the floor of one

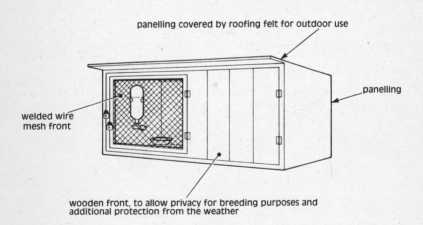

Fig. 2. A home-constructed single hutch with two compartments suitable for breeding purposes, for a single rabbit or for isolation. If the hutch is to be sited out of doors, a sloping roof, with a 5 cm (2 in) drop and covered with roofing felt, should be fitted.

The single hutch is the most universal form of housing and may be used with equal success for one or several rabbits. However, it does suffer the disadvantage of having the highest unit cost of all types of hutch. It is the ideal breeding cage and may be used indoors or out.

hutch is the roof of the one below. Providing that the floorboards are tight-fitting then they alone, without the use of sealants, will be satisfactory. Nevertheless, show specimens are best kept on the top tier to avoid any danger of staining from matter falling from the hutch above. Commercial units are available which incorporate a 50–80 mm (2–3 in) removable board below the wire front to facilitate cleaning. Alternatively, a removable aluminium tray or other light non-corrosive metal tray, 30 mm ($1\frac{1}{4}$ in) deep, which fits just inside the hutch with the lip outside of the door, may be incorporated into any system to reduce the time involved in cleaning.

HUTCH CONSTRUCTION

Hutches may be constructed from any soft wood on a 30 × 30 mm ($1\frac{1}{4}$ × $1\frac{1}{4}$ in) frame and the sides and floor/roof made of 8–10 × 1 cm (3–4 × $\frac{1}{3}$ in) panelling (Fig. 3). The door frames should be of 20 mm ($\frac{3}{4}$ in) square timber. The door itself is held in position by strips of wood placed behind the door so that it fits flush. The front is secured by means of a butterfly latch. It is not necessary to buy new timber for hutches as it is likely to become stained in a short period of time. Any sound secondhand timber, including thick floorboarding, may be used, providing that a stronger frame is employed.

Hutches of whatever design should be painted with a non-lead-based paint or treated with a wood preservative, such as creosote. This not only protects the wood from the elements, but it discourages the rabbits from chewing their homes. Once a rabbit has developed this habit it can be extremely difficult to cure. Recommended minimum hutch sizes are given in Table 1.

The six-hutch unit is one of the most popular sizes, and the design shown incorporates metal trays for ease of cleaning.

Table 1. Minimum hutch sizes for breeding purposes

Breed Size	Hutch Size		
	Length cm (in)	Width cm (in)	Height cm (in)
Small 2 kg ($4\frac{1}{4}$ lb)	60 (24)	60 (24)	60 (24)
Medium 2–4 kg (4–$8\frac{1}{2}$ lb)	90 (36)	60 (24)	60 (24)
Large over 4 kg (over $8\frac{1}{2}$ lb)	135 (54)	60 (24)	60 (24)

MORANT SYSTEM

The morant system is ideal for raising rabbits that will not reach exhibition

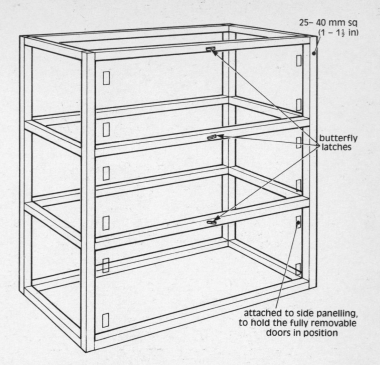

25– 40 mm sq
(1 – 1½ in)

butterfly
latches

attached to side panelling,
to hold the fully removable
doors in position

Fig. 3. A three-storey system of hutches: (a) framework; (b) detail of door fitting. Note that all-wire fronts should be used for indoor rabbitries, but where hutches are kept out of doors half of the front should be covered with wood to afford the rabbits adequate protection.

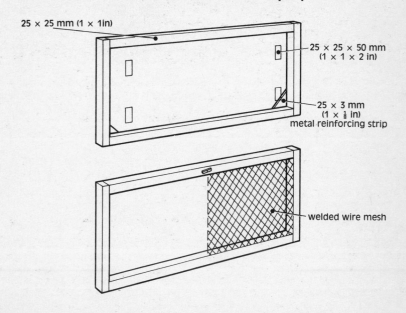

25 × 25 mm (1 × 1in)

25 × 25 × 50 mm
(1 × 1 × 2 in)

25 × 3 mm
(1 × ⅛ in)
metal reinforcing strip

welded wire mesh

standard, in a colony, until they are large enough for the table (Fig. 4). The morant consists of run, triangular in cross-section, attached to a large movable hutch.

The structure of the run is designed to reduce weight and costs. The whole system is moved daily over an area of grassland or rough lawn. Whilst the grass does not provide all of the food necessary, and a supplement of pellets should be fed, feeding costs are reduced considerably and the system is useful during the spring and summer months when there may be too many youngsters for the hutches available to house them.

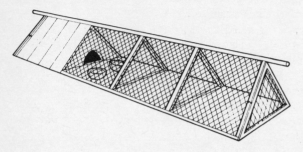

Fig. 4. The Morant system, for use when raising rabbits to the age of four or five months.

WIRE CAGES

The most popular method of housing in commercial rabbitries is wire cages. These have the lowest unit cost and are designed with a tray beneath them to catch the droppings, which pass through the wire-mesh floor. Such structures are readily cleaned and washed in agricultural disinfectant, and represent a useful method of raising meat stock. They are not suitable for the fancier who tends to keep his stock until they are older, by which time sore hocks will probably have developed as a result of the wire-mesh flooring.

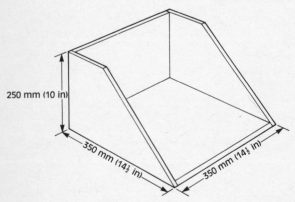

Fig. 5. A nest-box for use in all-wire cages.

Because no bedding is used in wire cages, it is essential to maintain an adequate quantity of good-quality hay to provide a fibre supplement. For breeding does it is necessary to place a nest-box in the cage (Fig. 5).

EQUIPMENT

FEEDERS
Unless the food is placed in a container, the stock, especially youngsters, will scratch the pellets onto the floor of the hutch. Even if some of the food is eaten from the floor, wastage results as the digestive system cannot deal with powdered foods as effectively as pellets. Either use a heavy-bottomed bowl or a cut-down can wired to the door of the hutch, making sure that there are no sharp edges on which the animal could cut itself.

DRINKERS
Purpose-made small-animal drinkers, consisting of a glass or plastic bottle with a tube leading from the lid and containing a small ballbearing to act as a valve, may either be bought at a pet shop or made from an old medicine bottle and some rigid plastic tubing. The alternative is to use half-moon-shaped drinkers which can be fitted to the front of the cage. Care must be taken to ensure that the animals cannot spill the water, otherwise the bedding will become wet and soiled. Stains on the pelts caused by soiled water are virtually impossible to remove. Both feeders and drinkers must be washed out regularly to stop the spread of any infection.

HAY RACKS
A small V-shaped rack, about 25 cm (10 in) long and 75 mm (3 in) wide at the top, should be attached to the side of the hutch for holding hay and greenstuffs. This ensures that the food is not trampled into the bedding, which would lead to stains and, in the case of cabbage, an objectionable-smelling rabbitry.

NAIL-CLIPPERS
A pair of sharp nail-clippers designed for animals, which can be obtained from any good pet supplier, must be kept in the rabbitry.

SCALES
It is necessary to weigh rabbits regularly to ensure that they are developing at the correct rate and that, for show purposes, they are within the specified weight limits for the breed. A pair of flat pan scales will be required.

TABLE
For examination from the earliest age a table or bench should be available. Cover it with a hessian sack to avoid the animals slipping.

FOOD BINS

A dustbin or other large vermin-proof container should be provided to store pellets and/or grain. Rabbitries readily attract rats and mice, and under no circumstances should foodstuff be left unprotected.

TRAVELLING-BOXES

In order to transport rabbits to shows, you will require one or more travelling-boxes (Fig. 6). These need to be lightweight and should be constructed of plywood on a 12.5 × 12.5 mm ($\frac{1}{2}$ × $\frac{1}{2}$ in) frame. The bottom section of the box should measure 450 × 300 mm (18 × 12 in) × 200 mm (8 in) high. It should be made entirely of plywood. This section should be hinged to another of the same length and breadth but of only half the depth (100 mm/4 in). The top of the upper section is covered in plywood and the sides are made up of 25 mm (1 in) welded wire mesh. A clasp is fitted to the front of the box. Inside, on one of the side-base sections, construct a cardholder in which prize awards can be placed. This is done by nailing two pieces of lath, 25 mm (1 in) wide and 150 mm (6 in) long, 125 mm (5 in) apart. Fix a piece of lath 125 mm (5 in) long at the base, and cover the whole

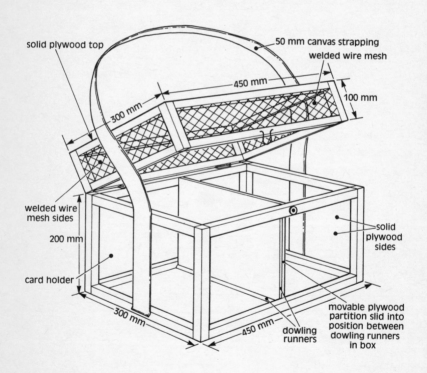

Fig. 6. An easy-to-make travelling-box.

with plywood. Attach a piece of canvas or leather to the sides of the box to act as a carrying strap.

Such a box will be sufficiently large to transport any rabbit over considerable distances. For smaller breeds the length of the box may be reduced by 100 mm (4 in); all other dimensions should remain the same.

It is possible to buy ready-made travelling boxes. These are often of a more complex design, but are equally effective.

MAKING A START

SELECTING A BREED

Unless you are certain which type of rabbit you wish to breed, visit several shows to study the different breeds and varieties that there are to choose from. Initial information concerning the venues of rabbit shows can be obtained from any local club whose address should be available from a public library, hobbyist journals or any national rabbit association.

Before settling on a breed decide the purpose for which the rabbits are required: meat, fur, wool, the pet trade or a combination of two or more of these. It is also wise to conduct some market research in order to determine which type of rabbit you can sell and the approximate quantities. This is particularly important if you intend disposing of your surplus through the pet trade.

MARKETS

MEAT RABBITS

The choice of meat rabbits is fairly wide; any large breed can be adapted to the purpose and New Zealand Whites and Californians are particularly popular with several farmers. Flemish Giants, Giant rabbits and Chinchillas have also all been used successfully for the carcass trade, with the bonus that Chinchilla skins fetch amongst the highest prices of all rabbit pelts, if you can find a suitable specialist market. Some meat-producers prefer to use F_1 hybrids, believing them to provide larger litters that reach maturity sooner. Backyard rabbit-meat production for home consumption is one of the few ways in which it is possible to raise your own meat at home. Moreover, it is a way of ensuring that the flesh has been produced without the addition of artificial substances and that the animals have been raised under conditions of which the owner approves. Many rabbit-fanciers, to deal with the problem of disposal of excess stock, eat their surplus animals. This goes some way towards defraying the cost of the hobby or, with careful management, may even give an acceptable return for the labour involved.

PET TRADE

Currently the pet trade in the UK is mainly interested in Netherland Dwarfs, a fashion which is likely to continue as the breed requires smaller hutches and consumes less food as well as retaining part of its youthful appeal even into the adult form. Pet shops are not only far readier to buy this breed, taking them when they refuse all others but are quite often happy to pay up to twice as much as for other breeds that are far more expensive to raise. Breeding Netherland Dwarfs for the pet market can, without difficulty, show a profit and, should you live near to a large town, it is highly likely that you will not be able to satisfy the market. Since the Dwarf is known in more colours and patterns than virtually any other breed, and the large number shown provides the keenest competition, it is not a breed to dismiss lightly if you intend keeping one particular type of rabbit.

Other methods of disposing of stock include advertising in local shop windows and, if all else fails, sending rabbits to a country market. These seldom achieve worthwhile prices and, in addition, the vendor has to pay the auctioneering costs. Several shows, especially those included as part of a major agricultural show, will often sell live rabbits and this can represent one of the best markets of all, as what child can resist a bunny? Shows charge commission, usually 10 per cent, to aid finances.

RESEARCH
Providing rabbits for research is a very specialist activity, and it is necessary to establish not only an agreement before seeking to breed for this purpose, but also the legislature of the relevant country relating to the breeding and keeping of animals for research. Usually, a particular breed of a specified age and weight will be required on a regular basis. Whilst breeding for this purpose is well established, it is impractical to consider it as a backyard activity.

RABBITS FOR EXHIBITION
The fancier whose main aim is exhibiting, and who keeps the rabbits for their own sake, will not be too concerned with markets for the stock. Nevertheless, careful thought must be given to the number of rabbits that can be kept and whether this restricts the owner to one or more breeds. During the spring and summer months, there will be pressure on hutch space. Therefore it is essential that no more breeds are kept than can be adequately accommodated. Where more than one breed is kept, the minimum number of hutches required is six per breed, although more is preferable. One way in which hutch requirements may be reduced is by keeping two or more colours of the same breed, e.g. Blue and Black Rex, and cross-breeding. Whichever breeds you decide upon, it is important that there are always spare hutches available to run on stock, to see whether they can fulfil their early potential. You will not want to dispose of a promising youngster simply because of insufficient hutch space.

SPOTTED RABBITS
It is possible to establish whether spotted rabbits have any show potential from the day they are born, as their markings do not change throughout life;

23

thus you can dispose of unsuitable specimens at an early age or foster them out. Not all rabbits that appear satisfactory on day 1 will grow into champions. It will still be necessary to allow the young to develop because, as they grow older, the pattern will increase in size and any minute blemishes, not apparent in the young kitten, become significant as the animal develops.

Because marked rabbits can be selected at an early age, the number bred in the average stud is greater than that of other breeds. Also, as far as showing is concerned, marked rabbits continue to win for longer than other breeds. The combination of these two factors has resulted in very high-quality rabbits being produced in these breeds. In many respects, marked rabbits offer the greatest challenge to the fancier, but once you have bred that all-elusive 'flier', it will often win Duplicate classes through to Best in Show.

OTHER FANCY RABBITS

Type and body structure are important with all rabbits but, in some, it tends to be a dominant factor. The Netherland Dwarf, Polish, Belgian Hare and Lops all depend to some extent on the exaggeration of one or more body features. Therefore the majority of such rabbits must be kept until they are adults before it can be established with any degree of certainty whether they will be of the quality desired. Himalayan rabbits are another breed with which the owner must be prepared to show patience as the markings do not appear until after the first moult.

FUR BREEDS

Although the nature of the fur that the animal will eventually possess is, to some extent, determined before the animal is born, it will not be for some time afterwards that the breeder can establish which animals will be worth keeping. It may be necessary therefore to keep several youngsters beyond 6–8 weeks, the age when they are disposable at the pet shop. It is usually impossible, in all but a few cases, to determine coat quality with any degree of certainty until the intermediate stage has been reached, but initial selection can be performed on the basis of coat colour. Although this also changes with age you will quickly learn to establish which juvenile colour will never result in an adult of the correct hue. Elimination may also be based on mismarkings; even a Self-coloured rabbit may well carry white hairs and these will never disappear, as the tendency for white hairs to appear in the coat increases with age. One of the most readily apparent signs of failure are eyes that do not correspond with the breed standard. Such rabbits, in any breed, may be disposed of at an early stage. Rexes and Normal Fur rabbits depend mainly on the quality of the fur. This does tend to deteriorate with age and, as a generalisation, it is necessary to keep fairly large numbers to ensure a consistent number of show animals. Another factor to consider when selecting a breed is whether the rabbitry is situated inside or out. If the hutches are outside in a position where there is a chance of strong sunlight, avoid any chocolate or brown rabbits as these can fade to a mealy colour very quickly. If there is any danger of the rabbits becoming extra cold as a result of your location, rabbits containing the Himalayan gene, including the Sables and the Smoke Pearls, should be avoided as extra markings may develop as a result of low temperature which has been shown to trigger the development of colour. However, it is possible to alter the living conditions to accommodate any breed and it is practical to raise any variety in virtually all locations, so that the would-be fancier has a free choice of the breed he would like to keep. It should be borne in mind that the Fur and Angora rabbits, especially the white varieties, must be kept spotlessly clean, so some thought should be given to the amount of time that you have to give to your stock.

BUYING THE INITIAL STOCK

Once you have decided which breeds you wish to keep you must now seek to obtain the initial stock. Months or years of frustration can result from a poor start. Do not rush into buying stock. Firstly, familiarise yourself with the breed standard and, more importantly, how judges interpret it. You cannot hope to breed top-quality stock unless you know what is being sought. You must get clearly in your mind exactly what is called for. Attend shows and study winners, then ask yourself what is the exact shade of the winning animal. No matter how carefully a breed standard is written it can never describe accurately in words the delicate colour differences between shades. Look for any special terms in the standard of your chosen breed and, as soon as you have decided on a potential seller of stock, ask him about the terms. He will be able to show you pea spots, teat marks and butterfly smuts if they apply to the breed. He probably will not be able to show you all the faults as many of them will have been eliminated from his stud, but he will be able to explain such terms as putty nose, barren feet and wall eye – all very serious faults or disqualifications. Fur is determined by feel. Ask to feel examples of soft fur, harsh fur, dense fur and sparse fur. Until you are fully aware of what the winning animals are like in every respect, resist any urge to buy.

When assessing the success of a particular stud, it is important to know not only whether it is winning its breed classes, but the degree of success it enjoys in the Duplicate Classes. This is particularly important with those breeds that have very small entries in their classes. Where a rabbit has only beaten a small number of competitors it is impossible to assess whether or not it has real quality. Try to establish how long the stud has been winning, as it is more likely that the rabbits possess the correct genetic make-up if they have been winning for many years. Having decided the source of your stock, you must expect to pay a fair price as it may represent several years', possibly a life-time's, work on the breeder's part in advancing the stud to its present level. Yet money alone will not guarantee success. Those who have paid large sums have seldom obtained a sound stud on this basis alone, and you should avoid the temptation to spent exorbitant prices for your initial stock.

In the UK and other countries in which breeders do not supply and, in many cases do not even keep, pedigrees, you will have to rely entirely on the information provided by the breeder concerning the ancestry of the animal. Discuss the breeding fully with the vendor, establishing how closely the animal has been bred and whether you could return a doe later for a mating, with a view to continue the programme. If you intend to do this, try to see as many ancestors of the rabbit as possible and try to establish in your own mind if standards are maintained and improvements are being achieved.

In the USA, with its strict registration and pedigree system, the ancestry of each animal will be documented, but this does not obviate the need thoroughly to examine the rabbit's relatives.

ESTABLISHING THE STUD

Unless you are intending setting up a full-scale commercial operation, do not buy too much stock initially as your numbers will soon increase and it is far preferable to have home-bred stock than purchased animals in the hutches. There are several approaches to establishing a stud. Probably the best is to buy the best-quality buck that you can obtain and two unrelated does. This will allow you to develop two distinct lines, both bred back to the quality buck upon which the stud will be built. By employing the two unrelated does there should be no need to bring in new blood in order to introduce new vigour for a few seasons. By the time that it is required you will have become established and better placed to decide the exact nature of any outcross that you may need to introduce.

Starting with one buck and two does from the same rabbitry, the generally agreed best approach will simply result in an extension of the strain originally developed by another fancier, and this means you have less prospect of breeding your own line of winners or improving the breed independently, which must be the long-term aim of every true fancier. It is possible to start with just one doe and have it mated by the original supplier. This will result in a far slower establishment of your stud, but, providing you buy from a good line, it can represent a sound start for a very modest investment. Using such an approach it is best to purchase from a local source to which you can return in the future as, even though you will not own the original buck, it may well be sound husbandry to use it as the basis for either line- or in-breeding.

Whether it is best to buy young or old stock is debatable. Unproven stock is not only cheaper but may give better results, in spite of there occasionally being problems with first litters. With proven does, the breeder is very unlikely to sell you a mother who has, in the past, produced top-quality stock as he will prefer to keep her for his own breeding programme. The sort of doe that you are likely to be able to buy is one which is approaching the end of her breeding life or one that has not lived up to what was expected from her. With a maiden doe, she will be of high quality, otherwise the breeder would not have retained her and there is always the possibility that she herself will yield winners. With the buck, it is absolutely essential that he has quality, because far fewer bucks are kept, seldom more than one for every six does. The only ones liable to be kept past the intermediate stage will be those that can combine the dual role of exhibit and sire. Any buck purchased should at least have been placed in a class or capable of picking up a card, otherwise breeding back to him is unlikely to develop the correct genes within the strain. If you cannot obtain such a specimen then pay to have your does mated until such a time that you breed a youngster with sufficient quality to become your stud buck.

Table 2. Factors affecting the Profitability of Rabbit-keeping

TOTAL COSTS		TOTAL INCOME
Non-recurring	*Recurring*	
1. Initial stock and new blood (can be recouped by selling and breeding stock) 2. Hutches, housing and equipment (written off by hobbyists; commercial rabbitries will include in costs and will be concerned with the profit per cage)	1. Food (cost depends on conversion ratios) 2. Straw, hay and other non-food consumables 3. Show entries, travelling and journals 4. Labour costs (applicable only to fully commercial operations)	1. Sales of pelts, Angora wool etc 2. Sales of live rabbits (depends on percentage raised to marketable weight: high market weight for the carcass trade – a virtually infinite market; low market weight – dwarfs have the lowest – for the pet trade – a very limited market; also depends on the number of does kept, and the average litter size – live weight) 3. Sales of show stock, breeding stock, and stud fees (depends on quality of stock and hay, and it can take years to establish the necessary reputation)

MANAGEMENT

ROUTINE

The rabbit is not a very demanding animal but, as with all forms of livestock, a routine is essential. Food may be given once or twice a day. The actual number of meals is not important as the rabbit will make several trips to the food hopper, preferring to eat spasmodically as it would in the wild; presumably the digestive system is most efficient under these conditions. The greatest quantity of food is consumed during the period of darkness. For stock animals, weekly cleaning out is required but, for exhibition animals, especially those with white or light-coloured coats, daily replacement of the bedding is necessary.

After soiled bedding has been removed, the remaining traces of excrement should be scraped from the corners of the hutch which is where disease-causing organisms are likely to breed. The incidence of disease and the danger of its spreading is greatly reduced by good hygiene. All hutches and equipment should be scrubbed periodically with a good proprietary disinfectant, but never use bleach. Do not return animals to a hutch until all traces of the smell of the cleaner have disappeared. Where large numbers of rabbits are kept, the dangers of disease are increased and hutches should be disinfected each week. The easiest type of hutch to keep clean is one which incorporates a movable metal floor. With wooden floors, it is advisable to obtain or make a hutch tool to facilitate the removal of soiled litter from the corners of the hutch – a position where the floorboards are more prone to rotting and infection is more likely to remain as this is the area which many rabbits use for excretion. The tool is made from a piece of mild steel 150 × 100 mm (6 × 4 in) welded to a 10 mm ($\frac{1}{2}$ in) mild steel rod.

Urine will cause staining of the coat and even bleach it entirely, ruining the rabbit for exhibition purposes until the next moult is complete. Even when the vulnerable belly fur is unmarked, the region beneath the hocks will become soiled unless you have a good routine for cleanliness. Stained hocks will cause the judge to mark down on condition. Urine is responsible for the white or reddish-white deposits which are seen in the corner of the cage and are the result of the accumulated deposits of salts passed in the urine.

Where rabbits have become lightly stained, providing that you spot the condition sufficiently early, it is possible to clean up the affected part with a wet or dry dog shampoo. Using dry shampoos, it is essential that all traces of the powder are brushed out. It is also possible to use ordinary shampoos, but where wet shampoos are used the animal must be thoroughly dried to avoid the danger of chilling. It must be stressed that shampooing should only be used in extreme cases and restricted to small areas. Rabbits should not be bathed.

Much of the danger of staining can be eliminated by placing a layer of sawdust or shavings about 10 mm ($\frac{1}{2}$ in) deep underneath the main layer of bedding. Sawdust containing large quantities of powder must be avoided, as some rabbits, especially bucks, tend to scratch and this can lead to dust getting into the eyes, causing weeping and possibly leading to infection. Dust or shavings from red woods should similarly be avoided as these, when wet, will readily stain pelts. A suitable supply of shavings can usually be obtained from a wood-machining shop, whose proprietors are usually very pleased to find someone prepared to remove them.

BEDDING MATERIALS AND MANURE

Any good-quality straw may be used, but you do not want old straw and the short-stemmed type is to be avoided if possible. Bracken, dried leaves and even lawn mowings, providing that they have first been thoroughly dried, may all be used. However, unless you have a very small stud this is not likely to be a practical proposition. Rabbit droppings and bedding are rich in nitrogen, potassium and phosphates and make excellent manure, providing the soil with all of the major plant nutrients and simultaneously building up the humus level. Never use the manure fresh as it will burn the roots of the plants. Instead, stack it at the bottom of the garden for about a year, turning it every three or four months.

ISOLATION HUTCHES

One or two hutches should be set aside from the main rabbitry as isolation hutches. These may be used to house sick animals and new stock. A new acquisition can bring disease into the rabbitry, so always keep it separate from the other animals for at least a month until you are sure that there is no danger of infection. Do not use it for stud purposes during this period.

From time to time, rabbits should be moved around to new hutches in order to allow the wood to dry out thoroughly. Not only does this reduce the danger of infection but it also reduces the likelihood of rotting and lengthens the hutch's life.

MEDICAL INSPECTION

Every rabbit should be inspected regularly to ensure that it is in good health. The eyes should be clear and show no sign of discharge. When this is found, the affected eye should be bathed and a veterinary eye ointment applied. Next the coat should be examined. A shiny coat is a sign of an animal in good health. If it is dull then the problem may be nutritional or something more serious. Note the onset of the moult which can result in the animal losing condition, and check for any signs of abrasions; these should be treated with a veterinary skin ointment. Fleas carry disease and they are responsible for the spread of myxomatosis. Should any fleas be detected, apply an animal insect powder and isolate the rabbit. Where a rabbit has been in contact with other rabbits, such as at a show, and you cannot inspect immediately for fleas, then it is advisable to place the animal in an isolation hutch. Every care must be taken to ensure that fleas do not enter the rabbitry.

Check that the rabbit is well muscled-up across the haunch. This is the first place where you are liable to detect any drop in weight. It is advisable to weigh the rabbits regularly and compare the results with their record card.

Finally inspect for vent disease, which is the term given to any infection of the rabbit's sexual organ. There is a rabbit syphilis which, fortunately, is fairly rare and it is not transferrable to humans. A septic infection resulting from bacteria entering via a cut or abrasion is far more common, and this can occur if there is insufficient or wet bedding. It is a sign of poor management of the stock and is totally avoidable. The treatment is to place the rabbit in a dry hutch with plenty of bedding and to treat the affected area with veterinary ointment each day until the problem has cleared up. Vent disease in its early stages is seen as a small pus-containing swelling. This will burst and the whole area becomes swollen and covered with sores. Whatever the initial source of vent disease, it is spread on mating and under no circumstances should any animal affected with the disease be used for breeding. The bedding of any animal suffering from the complaint should be burned and the hutch thoroughly disinfected before reuse.

Routine medical inspection takes only a few minutes per animal and should be performed once a week. It should also form the basis of the assessment of the health of any animal before purchase.

CHECKLIST FOR ESTABLISHING THE HEALTH OF A RABBIT
The following should be used as the basis of the regular health checks performed on every animal and before purchasing any new stock.
1. Check that the body is well rounded and covered with flesh – a sign of good nutrition.
2. Check that the eyes are bright and free of any discharge – a sign of good all-round health with no specific eye problems.
3. Check that the rabbit does not have buck teeth – sign of an incurable hereditary problem.
4. Check that the rabbit does not have fleas – sign of potential danger to the whole rabbitry.
5. Check that there is no discharge from the sexual organ – a sign that there is no sexually transmitted disease present.
6. Check that there are no traces of diarrhoea – a sign of scouring.
7. Check that there are no signs of cuts or abrasions, especially around the

lips or eyes, or bites on the ear – a sign of fighting due to keeping the young rabbits together for too long.

8. Check that there are no signs of sores on the hocks – a sign of poor housing.

9. Check that the animal is clean underneath – a sign of good husbandry.

10. Check the overall appearance, ensuring that the rabbit is lively and the coat is sparkling rather than dull – a sign of overall good health.

HAIR GROWTH

The quality of a pelt depends upon the density and the structure of the individual hairs. Hair itself is made up of dead cells which originated within the hair follicle; it is the number of follicles which determine the density. Follicles are formed in the embryo and their density will not change after birth. Although it may be difficult to detect the character of the pelt in the newly born rabbits it will have been determined in the uterus. It is dependent upon hereditary factors, the level of nutrition and possibly the number of young being carried by the mother.

The living hair cells divide below the bulb, which is the base of the shaft through which the hair emerges, and emerge as three separate layers: the cuticle (the thin outer layer), the medulla (the central structure containing empty spaces, which is absent from the tip and root portions of the hair), and the cortex, which is sandwiched between the cuticle and medulla. The nutrients reach the hair through blood vessels in the skin, but it is the size and shape of the papilla, which is a specialised dermal structure, rather than the level of nutrition, which determines the structure of the individual hair. The hair diameter is dependent upon the number of cells that are simultaneously dividing, whereas the length is a measure of the number of times that each row of cells has divided. At about one-third of the length of the follicle, the shaft containing the bulb and papilla into which the sebaceous gland secretes and where the hair erector muscle acts, the now dead hairs harden, as a result of the deposition of a protein called keratin. How many cells will develop and hence how long the hair shafts grow will be a result of, amongst other factors, the length of time for which the follicle is active. In no animal does hair grow continually. The hair follicle is active until growth is complete. It then undergoes a rest period, which, in the case of the rabbit, may be for several months, before regaining its activity. The new hair formed pushes out the old shaft.

Fur fibre consists of the very dense hairs of the smallest diameter that make up the majority of the coat. They are shorter in all but the Rex breeds and are not normally seen unless the coat is parted or blown into. Primary guard hairs (primaries) are longest and thickest of all hairs and are responsible for much of the overall appearance of the pelt. Secondary guard hairs (secondaries) are intermediate between fur fibres and primaries in both length and thickness.

THE MOULT

The result of the resurgence of the follicles' activity is the onset of the moult. Two types of moult occur within the adult rabbit, the most important of which is the wave moult in which the newly emerging hairs travel in a wave from the head across the back to the flanks. This may be seen as a wave of differently coloured hair moving across the back of the animal, the shade of the wave depending upon the colour of the fur itself. It is not possible to induce the onset of the moult or speed up its progress, but poor nutrition may well delay all stages. Shaving the hair does not stimulate growth, nor does plucking, except possibly just in front of the new growth line. It appears that this may go some way towards re-awakening the dormant follicle. Whether it does or not, the practice of keeping rabbits well groomed will result in the immediate removal of the old hair shafts from the pelt in the regions around the haunches. This is where dead hair remains long after it has disappeared from the rest of the body if combing does not take place. Progress of the moult in a coloured rabbit may be established by noting the appearance of dark-coloured skin patches, which are the pigment in the emerging hairs. It is not observed in white rabbits.

The onset and duration of the moult is dependent upon temperature as well as feeding. Whilst higher temperatures tend to stimulate growth, the process can be delayed in very hot weather as the rabbits may tend to be off their food. Housing the animals indoors or outdoors seems to have no effect on the duration of the moult or its onset. There appears to be little evidence for the occasionally quoted view that animals housed in an outside rabbitry have superior coats. After the first moult, which occurs between the fourth and sixth week, the rabbit appears to be in a state of continual moult up to the age of five to six months, or even longer, depending upon the breed and level of nutrition. Actually there are two distinct moults happening simultaneously.

Hormone levels may also be a factor that influences the moult and this will become more important after the third, or adult, coat has formed. For the rest of the rabbit's life, there will be a main moult during the spring period lasting for several weeks. This may be followed by a lesser moult, possibly not covering the whole body and complete before the end of the summer.

In addition to the major or wave moult a secondary moult is occurring almost continuously and results in the apparent random replacement of hairs.

Hair follicles develop in patterns. The primary follicle, in which the primary guard hair forms, appears first. This is surrounded by a group of secondary follicles in which both the fur fibres and the secondary guard hairs form. Information concerning the various breeds of rabbit is not available but, in the sheep, the one animal whose wool has been extensively studied, the number of secondary follicles surrounding the primary ones differs from breed to breed. This may well be the situation that exists with the rabbit. Those breeds with the denser coats and the greatest number of guard hairs have the most secondaries for each primary guard hair.

IDENTIFICATION
RINGING
The ideal stage for ringing the rabbit is when it is about eight weeks old. Ring earlier and it will probably shed the ring. Delay the ringing and you may find that the animal has developed to such a size that it is impossible to pass the ring over the knuckle of the knee. Rings are supplied in different sizes by the British Rabbit Council and it is essential that you use the correct ring for the breed of animal which you are identifying. Each ring bears the size of the rabbit, stated as a letter, as well as an identification number and the year of its birth.

To ring a rabbit, hold it firmly at the loins with one hand and, with the other hand, stretch out the leg slightly. Slip the ring over one of the back feet, taking care not to catch it in the small nail that grows some distance above the foot. Carefully pass the ring over the knee so that it rests just above the joint. This ring will stay on the rabbit for life and without it the animal will be ineligible for showing. Once a ring has been used on a rabbit it is not permissible to use it again. Providing that the breeder is a member of the BRC he may buy as many rings as he wishes. When a rabbit is sold, its ownership, through the ring number, must be transferred to the purchaser before it can be shown again.

TATTOOING
In the USA, an alternative method of identification – placing a tattoo in the rabbit's ear – is used. There is a range of devices that can be employed for this purpose, the commonest ones being a clamp with movable letters or a hand-held needle. It is usual to clean the surface of the ear with methylated spirit. A hand or electric needle is dipped into the ink and its tip allowed to penetrate just below the epidermal layer. Using a clamp, the ear is pressed firmly but gently and the ink is then immediately rubbed into the depression. Breeders may adopt a variety of numbering and lettering codes as it is the actual letters that are placed in the ear that are recorded on the registration certificate. In New Zealand both tattooing and ringing are permissible and, for imported stock, most rabbit associations have a scheme of mutual acceptance.

SEXING
It is desirable to know the sex of a rabbit from the earliest age. The youngest age at which it is practical to examine the sex organ is about six weeks. Holding the rabbit firmly, gently press the skin enclosing the organ with the thumb and forefinger. The buck will possess a tube-shaped organ whilst the female has a V-shaped organ with the greatest protuberance at the end nearest the head. Until you are familiar with the technique you may make mistakes; but a watchmaker's glass will greatly aid differentiation. At the

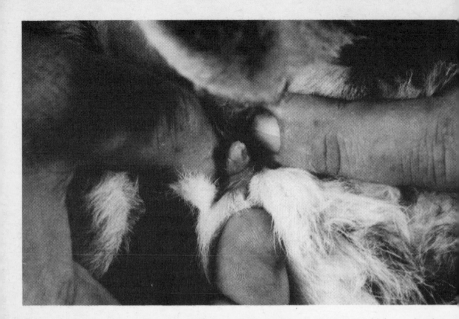

To sex a rabbit, gently press back the skin surrounding the sex organ, which can then be examined. The penis of the male is shown in (a) and the clitoris and vulva of the female in (b). Note the tubular shape of the male organ, and also that it is symmetrical, whereas the female organ is triangular with the longest side towards the head end of the animal.

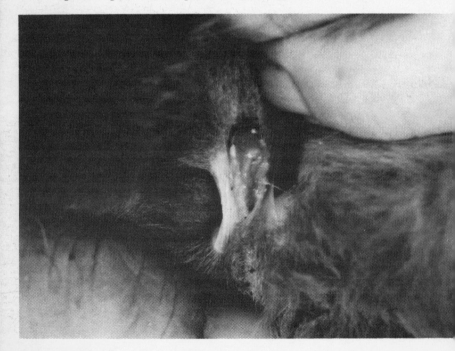

same age it is possible, to the experienced eye, to sex a rabbit on a secondary feature such as the size of the head. The head of the buck is broader, and larger relative to the body size, than that of the doe. Familiarise yourself with relative head sizes as this can be a quick and useful back-up method of sexing. By the age of about four months, the first signs of the testes emerging can be detected in the male. This is an infallable method of differentiating between the sexes until such time as you are competent to sex earlier in the rabbit's life.

NAIL CLIPPING

By the age of five months, the toe nail will have begun to protrude beyond

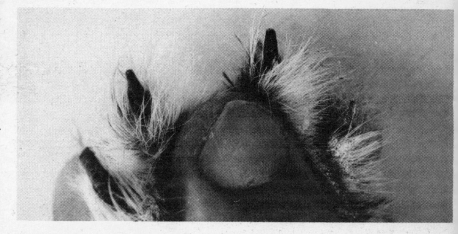

Nail clipping. When the nails have become overgrown (a), firmly grip the foot and, with sharp nail clippers, cut the nail (b), ensuring that you do not cut into the quick.

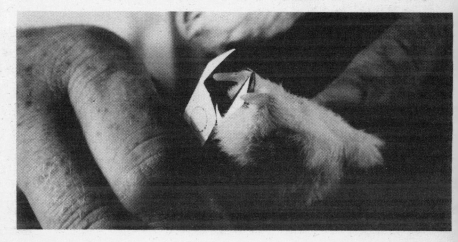

the fur of the foot, which has no pads. This is a sure sign that a rabbit has reached, or is approaching adulthood and it can be used to estimate the age of a doe (with the buck the descent of the testes through the wall of the abdomen is a more accurate guide). The nails, like the hair, consist of keratin. They continue to grow throughout life and those of domestic rabbits, which do not get worn down, eventually reach a stage where they need cutting. Nails may be cut with animal nail-clippers or sharp wire-clippers. With rabbit varieties that have white toe nails it is possible to see the blood and how far it travels into the nail. The nail should be cut well short of this mark. With darker-coloured nails it is important to remove only a small amount, to avoid bleeding. Should bleeding occur, apply potassium permanganate crystals to the nail. These will stop the bleeding. With clipping, the rule should be remove a little, often.

HANDLING

All rabbits should be handled regularly from an early age, not just for routine inspections, but to be groomed and posed as for a show. It is important to pick up the rabbit correctly. Never pick a rabbit up by the ears or the scruff of the neck. Instead place one hand under the stomach and the other across the haunches. Lift gently but firmly, with one hand beneath the belly transferring the weight to the haunches, and the other sliding towards the tail. The animal can now be lifted. To examine the underside of the rabbit, lift the animal and grip it firmly by the loins, taking all the weight with this hand. With the other hand, hold the rabbit firmly by the ears. The rabbit can now be stretched out, the back legs will be pinned firmly together and the underside of the animal can be examined.

Where rabbits have to be transported over long distances it is important that a proper travelling-box is used. This should be provided with bedding, but not pellets which tend to make the animals thirsty, nor greens which could stain the pelt. The rabbit will be able to sate its appetite on the hay. They can remain for long periods in the box which should be kept in the shade.

AGGRESSION IN RABBITS

The rabbit, by nature, is a timid and docile animal with no natural tendency towards aggression and, whilst the young are very frightened when they are still with the doe, they soon become a pleasure to handle. Gentle firm movements will give confidence to the animal. Aggression is born of fear and, if at any time the animal has been roughly handled or tormented, then rabbits will attack and bite quite hard on occasions.

The smaller breeds show a greater tendency to be aggressive but this does not mean that they cannot become as tame as other breeds, providing care is taken with them from the earliest age. Claims that these breeds have tendencies towards irritability are often related to their popularity with children, who perhaps are not as considerate as they might be.

Handling a rabbit. To pick up a rabbit, place one hand to the side of the animal and the other hand to the opposite side towards the rear (a). Gently but firmly grasp the rabbit behind the front leg and at the base of the opposite hind haunch (b). Now lift the rabbit, taking its weight on the hand which is supporting the haunches and using the other hand to control the animal

(c). Slide the non-supporting hand up to the base of the ears, taking no weight but using it to control the animal (d). (The animal should be completely supported by the other hand.) Apply gentle pressure with the thumb and forefinger, making it impossible for the rabbit to move.

KEEPING RECORDS

It is important that complete records of all rabbits are maintained, not just of their matings and show wins but of the number of young that are born and raised to weaning stage, together with the weight at all ages. Where pedigrees are not formally kept then these must also be maintained for use at home.

Pedigree forms (Fig. 7) are an indispensable part of a scientific breeding programme. Breeders are advised to maintain pedigree forms that are sufficiently large to allow space for a comprehensive record of the history of the rabbit.

It is advisable, wherever possible, to include the gene formula. Where there is some degree of doubt, such as a fawn-bred Orange Rex, then it may

37

Buck	Buck	Buck	Buck
Ring no.	Ring no.		Doe
Major wins	Gene formula	Doe	Buck
			Doe
	Doe	Buck	Buck
	Ring no.		Doe
Gene formula	Gene formula	Doe	Buck
			Doe
Doe	Buck	Buck	Buck
Ring no.	Ring no.		Doe
Major wins	Gene formula	Doe	Buck
			Doe
	Doe	Buck	Buck
	Ring no.		Doe
	Gene formula	Doe	Buck
			Doe

Fig. 7. Design of pedigree form.

be logged as *AABBCCDD/deerr*, the *D/d* denoting that either gene may be present, or more simply *D/deerr*, omitting the genes of the Agouti.

Each rabbit should be issued with a record card with its ring number or tattoo as the identifying feature. These can be pinned to the hutch, although it is preferable to paint a number on each hutch and keep the record cards in a loose-leaf folder.

To obtain the maximum benefit from record cards it is necessary to design them in such a way that they contain all the information that is relevant to the animal. Breeders may elect to design their own cards or they can use the style shown in Fig. 8. In either case it is best to place the record card on the back of the pedigree form and insert them in a loose-leaf ring-file.

There are computer programs available for the large-scale meat-raiser. Hobbyists may seek to adapt any simple program designed for the home computer to afford a video display of the records of the rabbitry.

When planning mating programmes, it is useful to produce a wall chart showing the relationships of all of the animals in a stud, as it is very easy to overlook one or more relationships. Where the rabbits are not homozygous for the major genes then the gene formula should be written under each rabbit. Such organisation requires very little time but avoids mistakes. Another way of increasing the efficiency is to place a year-planner calendar

Age in weeks	Weight in kg	Change in grams since previous weighing	Show record and other notes	BREEDING RECORD (Matings for bucks, litters for does)			
				Date	Mated to ring no.	Number born	BUCKS Notes on progeny
6							
8							
10							
12							
14							
16							
18							DOES No. raised to marketable age
20							
22							Average litter size
24							1987
26							1988 1989 1990
28							Percentage raised to marketable age
30							
32							1987
34							1988 1989 1990
36							No. of kittens
38							1987 1988
40							1989 1990

Fig. 8. Rabbit record card.

on the rabbitry wall, marking in the dates of each mating and highlighting with different colours the dates when the litters are due. Do not highlight the expected date of birth until such time as you have confirmed the pregnancy.

KILLING RABBITS

Whether or not you intend keeping rabbits for meat it is necessary to know a humane method of killing them. The method favoured by experienced rabbit-keepers is to pull the neck. This consists of holding the animal by the back legs with one hand and behind the skull with the other and giving a swift jerk. The pull must be sufficiently strong to dislocate the neck and kill the animal. Failure will cause the animal great pain and you should never attempt this method, unless you have been shown how and you have strong wrists.

Another instant method of killing rabbits that anyone can use is to take a very strong piece of wood, about the size and thickness of the rung of a chair, and to strike the rabbit at the base of the skull with full force. It is essential that the rabbit is not aware of being in any danger as otherwise the adrenalin level in the animal will be raised and will cause meat to remain tough after hanging.

As soon as the rabbit is dead, it should be hung by its back legs to allow the blood to drain to the head, ensuring that the flesh remains white.

SKINNING A RABBIT

To skin the rabbit, hang the carcass by one hind leg from a beam using a butcher's hook. With a sharp knife, make an insertion in the stomach region without cutting through the wall of the abdomen and cut towards the unsuspended leg. Pull the leg through the pelt, cutting off the pelt at the lower leg around the knee joint. Next suspend the animal carcass by the freed leg and remove the pelt from the other leg. Now pull the pelt over the body and the forelegs, cutting the skin away as necessary. Cut the head off the rabbit. Then remove the pelt.

To gut the rabbit make a cut about 70 mm (3 in) long in the abdomen and pull out the intestines. Pull the remains of the lower colon through the rear of the rabbit. Remove the offal (the heart, liver and kidneys) from the remainder of the intestines. If there are any white spots on the liver, it should be discarded. Such spots indicate that the animal was in poor health and the liver is not fit for human consumption. Situated in the liver is a jade-green sac, about 10×3 mm ($\frac{4}{10} \times \frac{1}{10}$ in) in size, containing the bile. Take care to remove this as its contents are bitter and will render inedible any flesh on which it is spilt.

DRESSING THE CARCASS

Top chefs will tell you that rabbit is the ideal meat for cooking. It has very little visible fat and, at the young age at which meat rabbits are killed, very little collagen, the substance that makes meat tough, has had the opportunity to form. The meat may be cooked by any method, including frying. The versatility of rabbit is greatly increased because it has no strong flavour of its own, unlike its wild cousin which often has a pronounced game flavour as a result of prolonged hanging (wild rabbits have the additional disadvantage that they are usually eaten at indeterminate age, old animals tend to possess a strong taste). This allows its use with the most delicately flavoured sauces, as well as strong accompaniments, such as curry.

Rabbit is also an extremely healthy meat to eat. The small amount of fat (less than virtually every other meat generally eaten, including chicken), coupled with the highest protein level, means that, if our present theories of human nutrition are correct, it is probably the best meat that we can eat. The home meat-raiser can, if he chooses, also control the diet so that no additives are included. Unfortunately, rabbit still retains some of its image as a poor man's food and the pictures of myxomatosis may still colour some people's attitudes.

If rabbit meat is to reach its deserved position in our diets then far more respect must be given to its preparation. In the past, its preparation has been

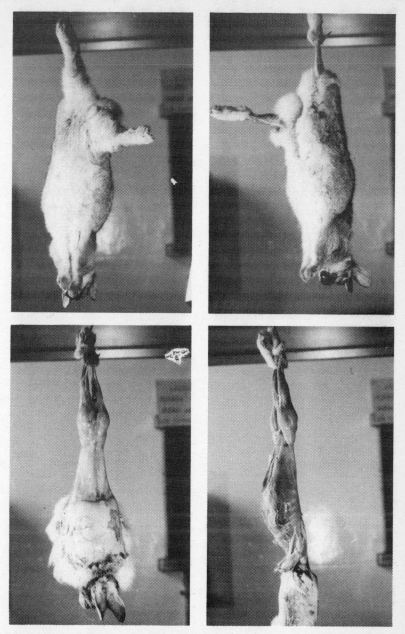

Skinning a rabbit. Hang the carcass by one leg (a). Release the pelt from each of the knees and cut the belly to the neck (b). Pull the pelt up towards the head (c). Free the skin at the front legs (d) and cut off the head immediately, taking care not to get any blood on the pelt. Should this happen, wash it off immediately. In spite of all the modern manmade fibres, it is impossible to imitate the pattern of the natural pelt (e).

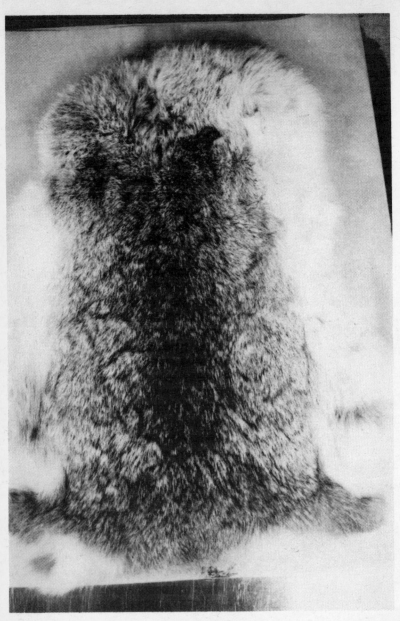

restricted to just a few very traditional dishes.

There are several ways of dressing the rabbit carcass, but probably few better than the method given to me by a multi-gold-medal chef aware of the culinary potential of the animal. After removing the stomach contents joint the rabbit by cutting away the fore and hind legs (Fig. 9). Cut the belly flesh

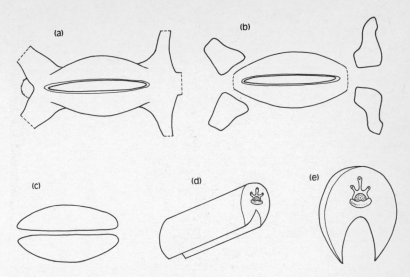

Fig. 9. Method of jointing a rabbit to produce quality cuts: (a) carcass with paunch removed; (b) the fore and hind legs cut away; (c) the belly flesh removed from the ribs in two pieces; (d) the back meat; (e) a cutlet.

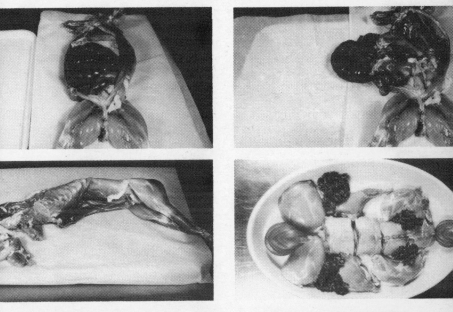

Dressing the carcass. The carcass is placed upon a tray and the abdomen is split open (a). The intestines (b) should be removed and the carcass jointed according to the instructions in Fig. 9, the front legs being removed first (c). Presentation of the carcass is important if the rabbit is to be restored to its former esteemed position on the menu. In (d), the skinned chopped back is surrounded by the rabbit joints and the whole is garnished with parsley. A decoratively-cut tomato is placed at each end of the dish.

away at the ribs to form two large strips of bone-free meat. Finally chop down the back to form a series of cutlets. The flesh may now be used in any recipe devised for similar-sized cuts. The extensive range of recipes produced for chicken may all be adapted for rabbit meat. The first chapter of this book mentioned how rabbit meat was included in the coronation feast of a king. It now just awaits imaginative culinary art to return to its rightful position in the cookery world.

TREATING SKINS

The skin must be dealt with immediately after removal from the carcass and may be treated in several ways. Where a large number of pelts are involved, air-drying is probably the best method. With varieties such as the Sable, involving a complex pattern, select only well-marked skins for the fur trade.

Before considering the treatment of skins, it is first necessary to establish the exact purpose for which the pelts are to be used. Large commercial operations will have established their markets, but the small stud-owner may find difficulty in selling the small number of pelts that he is likely to obtain and it will be necessary to store skins until a marketable number is available. With a little careful planning, the small operator should be able to develop a profitable sideline in dealing in pelts.

Rabbit skins are very versatile and they have a range of uses. Seek outlets through shops, craft fairs and exhibitions, the makers of toys, soft furnishings and handmade clothes. Patterned pelts, such as Sables, Smoked Pearls and Chinchillas, should find a ready market as it is impossible to match the delicacy and intricate variations of the natural skin with any manmade fibre. Self-coloured skins can also be sold for glove-, hat- and toy-making. Because of the money that can be obtained for pelts, it is worth going to the trouble of establishing your markets and not just to discard them, believing that in the days of modern materials there is little call for such specialist items. With the return to more natural products the market will increase rather than decrease.

Where the pelt is to be harvested it is important to select carefully the time at which the rabbit is killed. It must be when no moult is present otherwise the pelt will be practically worthless. With young frying rabbits this must be at a stage between the intermediate and adult coat and the selection of the killing time will be very critical. During the killing and skinning, no blood must be transferred to the fur; if this happens, it must be removed immediately. It is also important that the *whole* of the body pelt is saved.

Once the pelt has been removed it must be scraped with a blunt knife to remove all traces of fat. Attention to detail at this stage is of paramount importance. The pelt must then be stretched. This is best achieved by taking a piece of wire 5.0 mm ($\frac{1}{4}$ in) thick and 650–750 mm (25–35 in) long, depending upon the size of the rabbit, and bending it into a U-shape so that it forms a spring. Place the spring about 50 mm (2 in) above the head end of the pelt and attach the pelt by allowing a very slight overlap of the wire. The coat should be held in position on the wire with clothes pegs. Four pegs should be sufficient. Where the U of the spring is open, attach a bulldog clip with lead weights attached to the butterfly ends to the pelt in order to stretch it downwards. The pelt should be left to stand in a dry room, but not in direct sunlight, until it is dry. If the actual drying proves difficult, a hair drier may be used, or the skin can be chemically cured before being placed upon the stretcher. The simplest way of doing this is by rubbing potash alum (potassium aluminium sulphate) into the damp pelt. It is essential that the very edges of the pelt are treated as bluebottles and other flies lay their eggs on any untreated part of pelts. Pelts should always be stored or treated in a vermin-proof area.

ANGORA WOOL

The only market for Angora wool is the increasing number of home-spinners and these may be contacted through county craft associations. You may either sell the wool to these people, or pay to have it spun and then make it up into hand-knitted garments. Hand-knitted Angora garments should fetch a very high price, and retail outlets as well as spinners may be contacted. Do not give all of your profits away to someone else! The wool needs to be free of mats when it is harvested by plucking. This consists of taking a small number of single hairs between the thumb and forefinger and very gently pulling the hairs out. Do not cut the wool from the rabbit with scissors, as the shorter strands will not spin into top-quality yarns. By plucking the wool once or twice a year, at the time of the moult, it is possible, after spinning, to obtain an average of 250 g ($\frac{1}{2}$lb) of wool per rabbit per year.

NUTRITION AND FEEDING

THE DIGESTIVE SYSTEM

The digestive system of the rabbit (Fig. 10) is designed to process large quantities of vegetable matter. The most striking feature is the large caecum lying between the small and large intestines. It used to be thought that this served the same purpose as the rumen in cows, but rabbits do not possess the bacteria that are capable of synthesising essential amino acids from a cheap range of nitrogen products such as urea. The stomach acts mainly as a storage bag in which the acid level is adjusted and the gradual breakdown of the food commences. The bile duct and the pancreatic duct secrete digestive juices which contain enzymes that bring about the main part of the digestive process – the breakdown of proteins into amino acids and starches into glucose. The caecum is the part of the system mainly concerned with the formation of the hard and soft pellets.

High biological value proteins must be included in the diet and feeds designed for horses and cattle cannot be used to replace the more expensive rabbit foods. Unlike the ruminants, rabbits cannot digest fibre very effectively and, for this reason, on a natural diet, they need to consume large quantities of food relative to their body size. In spite of their inability to digest fibre, rabbits do require a certain amount of it if they are to utilise other foodstuffs efficiently. A rabbit will feed from twenty to twenty-five times a day but the duration of these feeds will decrease as the rabbit's weight increases. Adult rabbits tend to feed mainly at night, but the young feed throughout the day.

COPROPHAGY

Rabbits produce two types of faecal pellets: the normal hard ones, which are seen about the hutch, and the soft ones which are excreted mainly during the night and are eaten by the animal straight from the anus. The soft pellets are the result of prolonged gut action: movement between the caecum and the large intestine and back again. The soft pellets are rich in protein as well as in B group vitamins, which are formed by micro-organisms in the digestive system. In appearance they are dark chocolate in colour surrounded by a gossamer membrane, the whole being excreted in clusters. Although there is a build-up of nutrients in the soft pellets, this is not similar to chewing the cud. Cellulose is broken down by the enzyme cellulase. No mammals produce this enzyme, but some animals act as hosts for micro-organisms

46

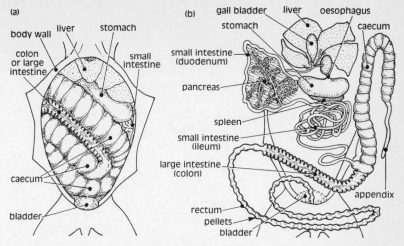

Fig. 10. The digestive system of the rabbit. The digestive organs are shown in position in the body cavity (a) and displayed to show their relationships to each other (b).

which perform the task in the mammal's digestive tract. The soft pellets contain bacteria which will cause changes in their composition, but the rabbit only incompletely digests the cellulose.

After about six hours, the material passes through the digestive system to be formed into further hard and soft pellets in the caecum; they also maintain by continued transference the micro-organism population in this part of the digestive system. Because the soft pellets are taken direct from the anus they will not be lost should the rabbits be kept on wire-floored cages, as is sometimes thought. The great danger of scouring is that the animal is unable to consume the soft pellets (sometimes shown by brown marks on the cheeks of the unfortunate animal) and is therefore unable to absorb nutrients properly.

NUTRITIONAL REQUIREMENTS OF THE RABBIT

For a rabbit to have a fully balanced diet, the following must be supplied.

CARBOHYDRATES

Sugars are required in small quantities (about 2.5 per cent of the total food) and are best fed as molasses. They are used to bind pelleted food. An excess may cause diarrhoea. Starches are widespread throughout all cereal crops and are the basis of pelleted food. Many root vegetables also supply large quantities of starch. Cellulose is the main source of dietary fibre. It is incompletely digested by the rabbit, but the diet must contain at least 15 per cent fibre if scouring is to be avoided. Where there is insufficient fibre in the

47

diet, the animals will seek to supplement their supply by eating their bedding or chewing the hutch. Carbohydrates are the main source of energy in the rabbit's diet.

FAT

This provides energy at over twice the rate gram for gram as carbohydrates, but it is not an essential part of the adult rabbit's diet. Some fat will be naturally present as oil in the plants contained in most diets. Fat is a vital constituent of doe's milk, which is far richer than cow's milk.

PROTEINS

The part of the body tissue which is neither fat nor water is protein; even the hair and part of the bone on which the calcium salts are deposited is protein. Protein is made up of several different types of amino acids, joined together. For each animal, there are certain amino acids that must be present in the diet every day. Indeed, in making up any diet it is essential that the correct amino acids are present. Any compounded foodstuff will have been carefully formulated to achieve the correct balance of these and other nutrients and for this reason, where such a food forms the basis of the diet, other materials should not be fed in large quantities as it could lead to dietary imbalance. Green foods can provide all of the essential amino acids, providing that there is a sufficient mix and that no food is fed exclusively.

VITAMINS

This is the name given to a variety of organic compounds that perform specific functions within the body.

Vitamin A Deficiency can result in a reduced growth rate and eye problems. It is unlikely to be a problem as most diets are rich in carotene, (which is found in green herbage), a substance which is converted by the body into Vitamin A.

Vitamin B This is a group of vitamins associated with the breakdown of food to release energy, the development of strong nerve cells and the production of new cells. Rabbits appear to have the ability to manufacture most of this group of chemicals from other food as a result of coprophagy. Thiamin, which is found in the bran of cereal products, is probably the only B vitamin that is required in any amount. Where the rabbit receives adequate cobalt in its diet – which will be in virtually every instance – there is no need to provide a Vitamin B_{12} supplement.

Vitamin C Unlike human beings, rabbits do not require large quantities of Vitamin C in their diet as they can manufacture it for themselves.

Vitamin D This is required for the deposition of calcium onto the bones. A deficiency will show itself as rickets, a disease in which the front legs of the animal are bowed. Vitamin D is also needed to ensure that the muscles function correctly.

Vitamin E This is probably the most important of all the vitamins, and a deficiency can lead to a variety of problems, including muscular disorders. The exact role of the vitamin in reproduction is not clear, but a deficiency can result in reduced performance in does. Coccidiosis is also associated with a shortage of this vitamin and it may be included as a supplement in some prepared foods.

Vitamin K   Needed for reproduction and blood clotting, Vitamin K is also often provided as a supplement in pelleted foods.

MINERALS

These are the inorganic equivalent of the vitamins and are required by the body for growth, as well as performing a range of biological functions.

Calcium   This is required for teeth and bones and in the absence of sufficient calcium the muscles are hyposensitive and move without an external stimulus. This can cause muscle spasms. Plants that contain large quantities of oxalic acid, such as rhubarb leaves, if ingested, remove calcium from the system, causing the muscle to seize up and the animal to die.

Phosphorus   Needed in conjunction with calcium for teeth and bone formation, phosphorus is also required for enzyme manfacture. Enzymes bring about all of the processes that occur in the rabbit's body.

Magnesium   This is also needed for bones; rabbits fed on a green diet are unlikely to suffer from a deficiency. A shortage may be one of the causes of fur-eating.

Sodium   Up to 1 per cent salt is included in diets, and it is the one substance, more than any other, that is responsible for maintaining the correct water balance in the body. Mineral blocks for licking can be obtained for rabbits. Extra quantities are required after scouring.

Potassium   Shortages can cause muscular problems as the element is present in the liquid surrounding the muscles.

Iron   Required in the production of haemoglobin, iron is the active constituent of red blood corpuscles.

TRACE ELEMENTS

Copper, zinc, manganese and selenium are all required in minute amounts. They are unlikely to be missing in the normal diet.

FEEDING

Correct feeding is just as important as the right breeding. Just as it is impossible to produce a winner from an animal that does not have the correct genetic make-up, unless the rabbit is correctly fed, from the time that it is in the uterus until it is an adult, it will never realise its full potential. Neither is it possible to correct any initial nutritional failings because of the differential rates of development of the various parts of the body. The bone structure, and possibly much of the muscle development, is determined long before the animal reaches maturity. Correct feeding must be maintained at all stages throughout the rabbit's life.

It is only in recent years that the results of scientific investigation into the rabbit's nutritional requirements have been available. Nevertheless it must be realised that the work carried out on rabbits has been an offshoot of the farming industry, which requires rapid growth rates, high protein-to-fat ratios and good conversion of feed into meat. Far less work has been done on the needs of the fancy rabbit, but it may be assumed that the basic requirements are the same, the only significant difference being in the actual amount fed. This will differ from breed to breed.

CHOICE OF FOODS

A balanced diet, offering a complete range of nutrients, may be provided by feeding either a variety of green materials, many of which will be natural to the diet of the wild animals, or compounded pellets. For all practical purposes, the rabbit-keeper need not concern himself with providing supplements to pelleted feeds as these should have been incorporated by the manufacturer.

Green Foods

Whilst it is still possible to maintain a small stud entirely on green foods, the greatest care must be taken to ensure that any wild food has not come into contact with weedkillers. Stale greens should never be fed, nor should they be given to the animals when the growth is too lush, as this can lead to scouring. During the summer months, when this is a problem, allow the greens to stand in the sun for a few hours. This is particularly important when greens are being fed to young stock or when they are going to be given to animals that have previously been on a pellet or cereal diet.

Wild Foods

Grasses   All members of the grass family may be safely fed but generally it is not a good idea to feed grass trimmings until they have been left in the sun to make hay.

Clovers   Both red and white clover are excellent, but red especially should be left in the sun before feeding. Large quantities, if fed whilst still lush, can lead to the bloats.

Dandelion   All parts, including the roots, can be fed, but dandelion is a diuretic and should only be given sparingly. It is better fed as a titbit than as part of the main diet.

Thistles   Perhaps the best of all foods, there appears to be no problems with feeding this weed. It is the ideal food for nursing does.

Plantain   All varieties may be fed but the broad-leaved type is probably best. Rabbits have been known to leave these if alternative food sources are available.

Docks   These may be fed up until the time that they are in flower, but not beyond.

Hogweed Available throughout the year but particularly abundant during the summer in the UK.

Comfrey This weed, found throughout the countryside near ditches and other wet places, can be cropped several times during the summer. When grown in the garden it probably yields the greatest weight of food (three to four crops) for the area of ground covered.

Hedge Parsley Another abundant food supply, this is found throughout the UK for much of the year.

Acorns Often recommended for rabbits, acorns are high in tannin and certainly not to the liking of all stock. They should only be fed in small amounts and it is probably not worth the effort.

Woody Growths The young shoots of heather, bramble tips, raspberries, blackcurrants and the prunings from fruit bushes may all be given to rabbits. Prunings are particularly good because the rabbits can wear their teeth down on them.

Garden Foods

Swedes, turnips and beet (including sugar beet, beetroots and mangolds) all make excellent fodder, but potatoes should never be fed either cooked or raw. Carrots are probably the rabbit's favourite root and it is usually possible to purchase large supplies of undersized roots from most greengrocers. Pea and bean shucks and the haulms of peas may be fed, as may all parts of maize (sweetcorn). Swedes, comfrey and stem kale are the best crops to grow especially for rabbits, but large quantities of cabbage leaves should not be fed to the exclusion of other materials as this will result in an unbalanced diet. Contrary to popular belief, large quantities of lettuce must not be given to stock.

Never feed any materials that are frosted or wet. In both cases stomach disorders will result. Always place green materials in a rack and remove any uneaten food before it has the opportunity to become stale.

Poisonous Foods

Never feed any food unless you know that it is safe. It is a fallacy that the rabbits will themselves know what is poisonous. They have been so long removed from a natural environment that they no longer possess the ability to differentiate between those plants which are edible and those which are not. Common poisonous plants include: laurel, ivy, bittersweet, belladonna, cultivated rhubarb and the wild form (rheum), honeysuckle, daffodil tops, potato haulms and arum lilies.

Pellets

The most convenient and reliable method of feeding is to use a scientifically formulated diet based on the established nutritional needs of the rabbit. Investigation has shown that rabbits take pelleted food and digest it far better than mashes. Pelleted foods will be wasted unless they are taken from hoppers, or from heavy-bottomed bowls which cannot be overturned. With pellets it is possible to control accurately the quantity that each rabbit obtains. This is critical in preparation of exhibition stock which are prone to obesity once they are fully grown. In the UK the typical composition of pellets is 60 per cent cereals and 10 per cent hay, the remaining 30 per cent being protein material providing the required amino acids and mineral and vitamin supplements. In the USA, alfalfa, which itself is rich in protein, can make up a very large part of the diet, together with grains. It is also possible to utilise by-products from the brewing, milling and cheese-making industries in the compounding of pellets.

Coccidiosis is a widespread disease aggravated by a reduction in the Vitamin E (tocopherol) level. An anti-coccidiosis supplement (ACS) is included in many pellets and it is in the interest of the breeder to feed pellets containing this supplement. A warning may be printed on the pellet container that stock should be taken off the diet for a specified time before they are killed for consumption. This is to avoid the danger of human beings ingesting the supplements and suffering from side-effects.

It is not necessary to use pelleted food entirely. Supplements of green material are eagerly taken up and will stimulate the appetite. Rabbits that have been brought up on pellets have been known to take green foods only after consuming all the pellets. The digestive system of the rabbit appears to be very sensitive to major changes in diet, such as replacing a diet of pellets totally with green food rations. Any transition of this type must be gradual, and extra attention must be paid to ensure that none of the green material is lush if scouring is to be avoided.

Rabbits tend to be very selective in their feeding. If they are used to a particular brand of pellet, they will ignore a new type until compelled by hunger pains to eat it.

Hay

It is only in recent years that the role of roughage in the diet of all mammals has become apparent, and the rabbit also requires dietary fibre to ensure good digestion and obviate the danger of loose droppings. Whilst pellets include fibre, a supplement in the form of good-quality hay should be provided. This is particularly useful with adult stock that are prone to obesity. Care should be taken, with young stock, to ensure that they are not eating too much hay at the expense of pellets, as this may result in the animals failing to sustain their growth rate. Where hay is not provided, the animals will eat their bedding straw; nutritionally this is inferior and, except in the case of young animals, hay should be available at all times.

Water

Rabbits need a constant supply of water. Where the water level is reduced they will stop feeding and a check in growth rate will occur. Where an all-green diet is fed, the water content will be well in excess of 75 per cent and water may be omitted, but a supplement must be provided for breeding does. Water is often blamed for diarrhoea but the real cause is a lack of fibre in the diet.

BREEDING

FEMALE REPRODUCTIVE SYSTEM

The reproductive system of the female rabbit is shown diagrammatically in Fig. 11. The rabbit, unlike many of the higher mammals, does not have an oestrus cycle. Instead, the release of the ova is triggered off by copulation. However, there is probably a semi-cyclic reproductive system controlled by the follicles which are situated in the ovaries. The development of the follicles themselves is controlled by a gland (the pituitary) situated at the base of the brain. This transmits the necessary messages which then trigger off the reproductive process. From the time of sexual maturity onwards, the ovaries produce hormones which make the female receptive to the male, and, for about three-quarters of this time, the female organ will be swollen and pinkish showing that she is ready to mate. During the autumn and early winter, the doe's capacity to produce these hormones is greatly reduced. Whilst artificial hormone injections are possible, these have no practical application outside of the laboratory and, possibly, commercial operations.

MALE REPRODUCTIVE SYSTEM

HORMONE AND FLUID PRODUCTION

The overall control of the male reproductive process, like that of the female, lies in the pituitary gland situated at the base of the brain. This stimulates the activity in the productive system itself (Fig. 12). The most important role of the pituitary gland is to cause the testes to produce hormones that govern the mechanism and behavourial aspects of fertilisation. Other glands (prostate and Cowper's) situated outside of the testes, produce the fluids which, mixed with the spermatozoa, produce the semen that is transferred via the penis to the doe.

Bucks reach sexual maturity between the ages of five and nine months, depending upon the breed, time of year and the level of nutrition. This period is four to six weeks longer than that required by the doe. In a mature buck, the testes will have descended through the abdomen wall and be plainly visible. It is a common belief that bucks will mate at any time but, during the autumn and early winter, the testes shrink and the male usually shows no interest in the female. It is probably the number of daylight hours more than any other factor that influences the seasonal aspects of sexual behaviour.

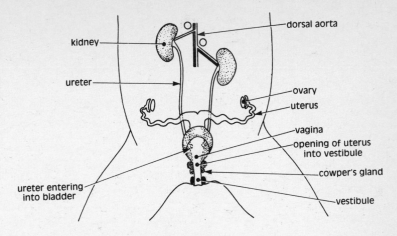

Fig. 11. Reproductive system of the female rabbit.

Spermatozoa

The cells containing the single chromosomes contributed by the male – the spermatozoa – are formed in the testes. A spermatozoa resembles a tadpole in appearance; the head contains the chromosome strands, and the tail provides the propulsion on entering the doe's vagina. Hundreds of millions of spermatozoa are produced each day and a single ejaculation can involve tens of millions even though only six to ten actually fertilise ova. The number of successful matings that can be performed by one buck each day will, amongst other factors, be a function of the number of sperm produced, and normally this will be sufficient for several servicings. There are reports

Fig. 12. Reproductive system of the male rabbit.

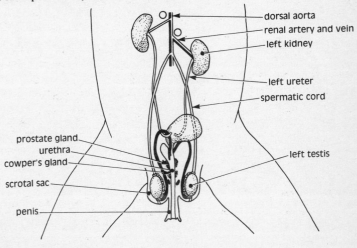

of large numbers of multiple matings performed by bucks, as many as thirty-two viable fertilisations in one day, but the average breeder is unlikely to require more than three or, at the very most, four matings from a single buck in any day. For short periods there seems to be no reason why a buck should not be used extensively as the sperm is available and there appears to be little scientific basis for restricting the use of a particular buck. Nevertheless, matings utilise large amounts of energy and the buck should not needlessly be kept with the doe. Neither is it necessary to allow him to copulate twice as is often the practice. With the high sperm counts normally encountered, if the doe is receptive then success will result from the first union.

DEVELOPMENT OF THE EMBRYO

The female releases her eggs about ten hours after mating and the ova meet the sperm in the oviduct. It is here where fertilisation, the combination of the male and female genetic material, takes place. The cells of the follicles change into bodies that are capable of sustaining the development of the embryos by producing chemicals that control the process. As soon as the new cell nucleus has formed, division starts immediately and the young kitten starts its life. After three days, the developing embryos leave the oviduct and enter the uterus. At this stage, nutrients are passed through the cell wall, but this method of nutrition is suitable only for the very limited period before the embryo implants itself in the uterus wall and a placenta forms.

At this point, there are separate circulatory systems for the mother and each of her offspring, but oxygen, nutrients and waste products can pass between the foetus and the mother across the walls of these systems which are in close proximity. Soon after implantation, it is possible to feel the young rabbits by the method of palpation (see p. 59). Any round structures felt before the ninth day – the time of implantation – will almost certainly be faecal pellets.

FINAL STAGES OF PREGNANCY

It is during the last third of the gestation period that maximum growth of the foetuses occurs and the diet of the doe should be gradually increased so that, after three weeks, it is double that of the maintenance level. Pregnancy is controlled by the now modified follicles and, during the final days of gestation, the chemical secretions trigger the birth mechanisms and probably the behavioural patterns in the mother usually referred to as 'maternal instinct'. This includes the loosening of the hairs of the chest and the urge to pluck them and to use them to build a nest. Milk starts to flow from the mammary glands, which increase quite dramatically in size during the final days of pregnancy. There are four pairs of teats and the milk, which is first secreted just after birth, will continue to flow in response to the stimulus of the sucking action of the young, but will gradually reduce between the fourth and fifth week when the kittens are weaned. If the doe is still in attendance after this time she will repell any kittens which try to continue feeding beyond this period.

RESORPTION OF THE YOUNG

In the wild, reproduction is a continuous process and the doe remates shortly after giving birth, from the late winter right through to the early autumn. Here the population level is controlled by the doe's ability to resorb her young if there is any danger of the size of the colony exceeding the food supply, thus recycling the nutrients involved in the production of the embryos.

In the domestic rabbit, the complex social structure that is such an important factor in this behaviour does not exist and, whilst hutch rabbits can still resorb their young, it is far less likely to happen where there is no competition for space and there is an adequate food supply. As a consequence, a doe will tend to overproduce in the early stages and, unless the correct level of nutrition is maintained throughout her life, subsequent litters will tend to be small and some kittens will be born underdeveloped.

To ensure that any rabbit bred for show develops correctly, it is imperative for it to receive sufficient nutrients from the time of conception, as different parts of the animal develop at different rates throughout life. Unless the kitten receives the correct food supply from the time that it is in the womb, all the various parts will not be in balance and, irrespective of how much food it may receive in later life, it will never have the good type that is essential to the show-winner.

PRACTICAL ASPECTS OF BREEDING

Rabbits, especially the smaller types, will breed from a very young age – four to five months. It is not, however, advisable to allow a doe to have her first litter before the age of eight or nine months, by which time she will be fully mature. A buck should not be used until he is nine months old. During the natural closed breeding season, it can be extremely difficult to induce rabbits to mate and produce litters, although, if the doe does conceive, she is unlikely to lose a litter even in the severest weather, providing that she has deep bedding and rain cannot enter the hutch. It is often not realised that successful matings can prove difficult at any time of the year if the animals are not in tiptop condition.

MATING

To mate a doe always take her to the buck's hutch, never *vice versa*, as she may attempt to protect her territory from the intruder and even attack the buck. Before attempting any mating, examine both animals' sexual organs to establish that they are free from disease, especially sores and septic lesions, which would be transmitted to the other animal. The female's organ should be reddish pink in colour and swollen, indicating that she is ready for servicing. If the organ is white and shrunken, she is unlikely to mate and will need bringing into season. A number of factors may be responsible for the doe's condition, but the commonest is nutrition. Check the weight of the doe. If she is underweight she is unlikely to produce and rear good litters. The number of eggs shed after copulation appears to be a function of the doe's body weight and this is one of the reasons why Dwarfs always have smaller litters than other breeds. Grossly overweight does will fail to conceive due to the deposits of fat around the ovaries.

DIFFICULT MATINGS

A doe which is reluctant to mate can usually be induced to do so by feeding *ad lib* for a few days. The process may be speeded up by removing the buck from its hutch and placing the doe in the male's quarters. The smell of the male is often sufficient to induce the female to mate without further encouragement. If the buck is placed with the doe for a few minutes each day, then the attempts to mate will further help to bring the female into season. Occasionally a doe will accept one buck and not another. The reasons for this are not fully understood, but it may be due to the new buck emitting different pheromones (sex attractants) to which the female may be more receptive. Where the exact mating is not critical, such as in rabbits being bred for meat or the pet market, a different mate may be tried. A combination of all of these treatments usually results in a successful union. Where it fails it is usually a sign of a major nutritional problem. Feed pellets *ad lib* for a fortnight before attempting any further matings. Does are capable of breeding throughout their lives but, after about four years of age, they often develop ovarian cysts, which stops them conceiving. Even when in very poor condition, bucks are usually eager to mate, except during the close season. An examination of the animal at this time will reveal that his testes have shrunk and it is pointless to put him to the doe at this stage. A good diet, together with the lengthening days, will return him to breeding condition. A buck may be bred from throughout his life, which may be twelve or more years.

In a successful mating the buck will fall backwards after mounting. If any other action occurs, such as the buck falling sideways, although it may appear that a mating has taken place, it will not be viable. It is often possible to check that successful mating has taken place by examining the female's sexual organ, where traces of the mucus-like seminal fluid should be seen. Even an apparently successful mating, however, will not always result in a litter.

PREGNANCY TESTING

It is necessary to establish at the earliest time whether the doe is pregnant. The first opportunity to do this is a week after the first mating when a second, or test, mating may be conducted. This consists of placing the doe with the original buck. She is more likely to reject him if she is carrying a

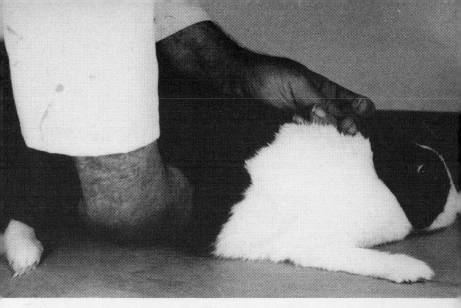

Palpation. Restrain the doe with one hand while using the other to feel gently whether there are any embryos present. These may be felt as marble-like objects from the ninth day onwards.

litter, but if she is empty she will probably mate, as the previous week's activity should have brought her into season. However this is by no means infallible. Some does will continue to mate even when they are carrying litters, whilst others will not mate although they are empty. It is not advisable to employ a different buck for a test mating as the scent of the new animal could, under some circumstances, cause the doe to abort her litter.

Palpation

This is the most reliable method of ascertaining whether a doe is carrying a litter and consists of feeling the developing embryos in the uterus. Familiarise yourself with the technique by gently feeling unmated does, noting the position of the faecal pellets of the digestive system, which are sometimes mistaken for embryos. Relax the doe; never try restraining an agitated animal, as the tensing of the abdominal wall makes detection far more difficult. Very gently feel the uterus which lies just forward of the pelvic girdle, applying only the absolute minimum pressure, to avoid any danger of damaging the embryos which, depending upon the breed, will for a medium-sized rabbit, be about the size of a pea on the twelfth day. This is the earliest time at which they can usually be detected. After twenty days the embryos are much larger and, whilst it is not advisable to delay until this stage, until such a time as you are confident about the position of the embryos, you may palpate a doe you believe to be mated to establish the position of the young (Fig. 13). Use this knowledge for future palpations.

After about twenty-one days, the mated doe will be considerably larger than when unmated. If the feeding has been correct, her sides will be swollen

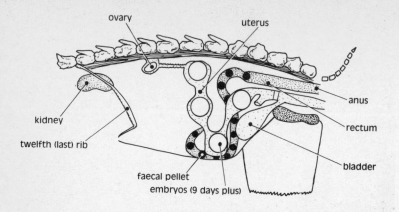

Fig. 13. Longitudinal section through a doe during the mid-term of her pregnancy, showing the relative positions of the foetuses and the faecal pellets after the ninth day of pregnancy.

and the area around the teats will begin to enlargen. This is a sure sign that she is going to have a litter. (As soon as it has been established that the doe is pregnant, she should be left undisturbed.)

PSEUDO-PREGNANCY

Occasionally a doe will experience a pseudo- or false pregnancy in which she displays many of the outward characteristics of being pregnant but, at the end of the gestation period, produces no young. The usual sign is for her to start pulling hair as early as seven days after mating, although in some cases it may be as late as the twentieth day before she starts plucking herself. When a doe commences fur-pulling very early she should be remated. If the behaviour does not start until later, check whether she is carrying a litter by palpating.

FORCED MATINGS

Where a doe continues to refuse to mate there is a method by which the breeder may aid the buck. Hold the doe firmly at the shoulders with the left hand, place the right hand under the belly of the doe and, with the thumb and forefinger, gently push the vagina until it is facing upwards and backwards. With the doe held in this position most bucks will mount although, whilst the mating may appear successful, it does not always follow that a litter will result. This again is due to the doe not being in season which, as well as causing her reluctance to mate in the first instance, means the ovaries will not shed eggs for fertilisation and, even if eggs are shed and fertilised, they will not develop.

ARTIFICIAL INSEMINATION

Due to the extensive use of rabbits in laboratories, the technique of artificial

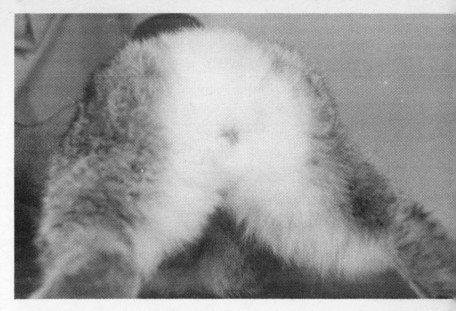

The forced mating. Grasp the doe behind the pelvic girdle and push the sex organ upwards and outwards (a), so making entry easier for the approaching buck (b).

insemination has been developed. This consists of encouraging the buck to ejaculate into an artificial vagina, transferring part of the seminal fluid to the doe and inducing ovulation by hormone injections. The technique is not practicable for the hobbyist or the commercial breeder.

PREPARATION FOR THE YOUNG

If the does is not already in the hutch where she will give birth, she should be moved into it a week before the litter is due. Ideally the hutch should be sited indoors but, if it is not possible, ensure that there is a compartment which is protected from the weather. This will provide the solitude that she requires when giving birth. Where the cage has no compartment, cover it with canvas the day before she is due to give birth. Disturb the mother only to feed her until you are sure that all the young have been born. The hutch should be thoroughly cleaned out and provided with a thick layer of bedding about five days before the litter is due. This obviates the need for nest-boxes – three-sided structures that some breeders provide for their does. Nest-boxes are necessary with the all-wire cages of commercial operations.

BIRTH OF THE YOUNG

The gestation period for a rabbit is thirty-one days but live litters can be born two days either side of this time. Usually about two to three days before the doe is due to give birth (although it may be as much as a week or as little as two or three hours), she will be seen running around the hutch with straw in her mouth. This is the sign that she is nest-building and that the behavioural aspects of the birth process have commenced. Where straw-carrying is observed some time before the doe is due to give birth, she will not usually build the nest at this stage and is simply satisfied to rearrange the bedding. Shortly before the birth she will pull fur from her chest and use it to line the nest. She will then be ready for the actual birth, which often takes place during the night. Absolute solitude is essential during the birth period. Any animals, such as rats or cats, will cause her to scatter and reject the young. Normal birth takes from one to six hours. A typical litter size is from four to eight. Does tend to have larger litters after the first one, but there are exceptions.

CARE OF THE NEWBORN

Rabbits that are used to being handled will not object to the contents of their nests being examined soon after the birth is complete. Give the mother a titbit and minimise the smell of human intrusion by rubbing your fingers in some hutch manure before very carefully removing the covering strands of straw and fur. At this stage any dead young, malformed or very small animals should be removed and destroyed. When the kittens are born, they are blind and naked, but it is possible to detect the hairs beginning to grow just below the skin. Fancy rabbits displaying spotting will possess their own individual pattern which will remain unaltered throughout their lives.

Obviously mismarked specimens may be removed at this stage as they will not improve with keeping. Do not attempt to differentiate between good examples of the Himalayan pattern.

Varieties other than white will have a coloured skin as a result of the emerging hairs. It is possible to sex the young on the first day as rudimentary sex organs and even mammaries may be detected. Very careful, quick and gentle examination is required, but at this stage the chances of error, and even damage, are high and it is best avoided, especially as it is only of minimal use at this time. As the hair grows it becomes impossible to observe the difference in the mammaries and this approach to distinguishing between the sexes is no longer possible.

MILK FLOW

Having examined the nest, replace the covering. Care should be taken to ensure that all actions are gentle yet positive; indecisiveness on the handler's part will be quickly transmitted to the animal. If, on the first inspection, you see that the nest is scattered and the youngsters distributed about the hutch, usually the litter can be saved. Build a nest from straw, line it with fur and return the youngsters to it. This problem occasionally occurs with maiden does and mothers whose milk has not started to flow. If the youngsters are found before they have had the opportunity to become chilled, they will usually be saved. It is more common to find just one or two young outside of the nest and these should be returned in the same way. Wandering youngsters are often a sign of the mother's inability to provide sufficient food so check that she herself has enough to eat. Young can survive for about three days without food, but will soon perish if their body temperature drops. Where the doe has clearly neglected the young they may be taken inside the house and kept alive with hot water bottles for about twelve hours before returning to the nest, by which time the mother's milk flow should have commenced. It is thought, with many rabbits, especially the wild type, that milk flow is often delayed until some time after the birth.

During the summer the wild animal mates soon after it has given birth and it was once thought that the milk would not flow until the mother had been remated. This is not true. With the hutch-bred animal, which has a good food and water supply, milk flow is not a problem, except very occasionally with maiden does. Because of the nutritional differences between does' milk and other forms of available milk (Table 3), hand rearing of young is virtually impossible. The high carbohydrate levels in cow's, sheep's and goat's milk will prove toxic to young rabbits and the low levels of fat and protein will lead to deficiencies.

It is sometimes said that the use of a nest-box with a 50 mm (2 in) front will stop the young escaping from the nest. This cannot be recommended as it is a problem rarely encountered in rabbitries and the nest-box would have to be placed in position before the doe kindled, and before it was known that she was a bad mother. Good feeding to promote milk flow is the only satisfactory approach.

Table 3. Composition of the milk of various mammals (in % whole milk)

Mammal	Constituent		
	Carbohydrate	Protein	Fat
Rabbit	1.9	12.0	10.3
Cow	5.5	3.3	4.5
Sheep	4.9	6.5	6.9
Goat	4.5	3.7	4.8

FOSTERING

Where a breeder possesses more than one doe, it is advisable to mate two or more on the same day. The mothers will kindle at the same time and, if one should choose to neglect her young, then they can be fostered onto one or more of the other does. The mothering instinct is so strong in rabbits that they will feed any young with which they are provided and they are not deterred by the scent of human beings or of the natural mother. Does will even foster young of a different age to their own. However, it is not advisable to have a litter containing young of an age difference greater than two or three days, as the larger animals may take the milk at the expense of the smaller ones.

When raising exhibition stock, it has been suggested that fostering be adopted as a routine procedure, using a breed such as a Dutch as a surrogate mother. Those Dutch young which are worth saving are retained and the young of the other breed are placed with the Dutch doe. The other doe, who no longer has to raise her own litter, can be immediately remated. In this way the number of potential winning young that can be obtained from any particular female will be maximised. Such a method is unlikely to appeal to the person who breeds rabbits for their own sake.

Nests should be examined daily to ensure that none of the young have died and that none of the kittens are failing to grow as fast as the others; both should be removed and destroyed. Young rabbits that fail to develop correctly in the nest seldom reach adulthood. It is very important, where close in-breeding techniques are being employed, that any youngsters showing imperfections are eliminated from the system.

Novice breeders who do not feel confident to interfere with the nest may delay until they feel that they possess the necessary experience. You can tell whether there is life in the nest by observing the straw or fur topping, which will be seen to move from time to time. The earliest advisable time at which to remove all the youngsters for a more thorough examination is nine days. With the doe occupied, place all of the young in a box lined with warm bedding. After thorough examination of each, return those to be retained to the nest.

REJECTION OF THE YOUNG

Rabbits are, by nature, good mothers. However, on occasions, they will neglect their young completely, leaving them in the nest to die. Where a litter is lost in this way, the doe will usually remate immediately. Should she neglect the subsequent litter, she should be destroyed as she is almost certainly a bad mother. Continual fostering should not be adopted, however well marked the doe or her young may be, as lack of maternal instinct could be hereditary instinct. Ignoring the young is most frequently associated with maiden does and no problem is usually encountered in later litters.

EATING OF THE YOUNG

From birth until about the seventh day, the mother may eat the limbs, heads or even the whole of her young. This will be due to the milk either failing to flow or drying up. Eating the young is part of the instinct to protect the burrow. By disposing of the dead flesh in this way there is no smell or blood to attract predators. Where cannibalism is observed, foster if possible, remate the doe and ensure that she has ideal conditions for the next litter, with no danger of disturbance, which will also cause her to destroy her young. Nervous does, or animals which are startled, will jump on the nest as a protective gesture, resulting in a squealing sound from the youngsters. The pliable bones of the kittens, as yet not fully encased in calcium and very supple, will not be harmed by the doe covering the nest. Allow them to settle down, and rearrange the nest if necessary. During the warmer weather, the doe may uncover the young from day one to allow adequate ventilation; do not cover the nest. In cold weather ensure that the nest is always covered and that there is a generous amount of bedding present, replacing any quantities that may have been consumed by the doe. Any excess of nest-lining material may be gathered up, sterilised by heat and retained for any doe that does not pluck enough of her own hair. This can be added to the nest; she will not notice if it is a different colour to her own.

LEAVING THE NEST

At ten to twelve days of age, the kittens' eyes will begin to open. One eye usually opens before the other, rather than the two of them together. Should the second eye not open for more than two days after the first, a bacterial infection may have set in. Very gently prise open the eye and apply antiseptic ointment. The young will start to leave the nest from about eighteen days onwards. It is at this stage that they will begin to take their first solid food, although they will still be feeding from the mother. At this point you must make sure that there is no lush green food in the hutch as this is the most vulnerable time for the youngsters and the period in which the greatest number is lost, especially through enteritis.

The young will continue to feed from the doe until the fifth to seventh week. It should be realised that, whilst the young will still prosper on the mother's milk, this will result in a large drop in the doe's weight and she may not be ready for breeding again for several weeks. It is advisable to take the young from the mother at the end of the fifth week.

Does can be remated on the day that they give birth, as usually happens in the wild rabbit. With the hutch rabbit, this approach should generally only be used with does who have just lost their young. The next time that a doe is most susceptible to mating is twenty-eight to thirty days after giving birth. If she is put to the buck at this time, she should not be returned to her young for, whilst rabbits will simultaneously nurse young and develop foetuses, this imposes a strain on the system that could result in the young not getting the necessary nutrients in the womb. Where a doe has been rested for some months, it is sometimes difficult to get her to mate and she should then be treated by the methods previously discussed.

NUMBER OF LITTERS PER YEAR

Fanciers are often satisfied with three or even less litters per doe per year, but rabbits in good condition, provided with a high level of nutrition, can produce six litters a year. Commercial breeders expect higher returns than this, mating almost immediately after parturition. A good doe can be induced to raise fifty to sixty young per year, although a more practical figure for exhibition stock, where type is all important, would be about half this number. A doe in good condition should be able to raise all of the young to which she gives birth, and there is no need to remove any from the nests. However many breeders adopt culling procedures to avoid becoming overstocked with rabbits that have no chance of winning. Where youngsters are removed in this way it does reduce the strain on the doe.

SEPARATION OF THE YOUNGSTERS

As soon as the mother has been removed, those rabbits which show any exhibition potential should be removed into their own hutch. Left together they are liable to damage each other. Non-exhibition stock that are being retained for meat production may, if hutch space is limited, be kept together until they are about three months old. After this, sexual maturity is beginning to be reached and the animals become aggressive and will fight. Young for meat may be 'finished off' in Morant hutches or wire cages.

Occasionally youngsters may be seen eating each other's fur. This is probably a nutritional problem because extra food soon stops the practice, as it does that of hutch-chewing, another habit which the young rabbit readily picks up.

THE GENETICS OF THE RABBIT

THE BASIS OF INHERITANCE

Modern domestic animals are far removed from their wild ancestors and better adapted to the needs of Man than to survival in the natural world. Man has produced the various forms and varieties to suit his special needs mainly by trial and error, without understanding how the changes which he was achieving came about. This century has seen tremendous advances in our understanding of the factors that influence heredity in livestock and, in this respect, more is known about the rabbit than possibly any other mammal. Due to the ease with which it can be handled, and the speed with which it can be induced to reproduce, the rabbit has been used in genetic experiments which have formed the basis of our understanding of inheritance in all mammals. Until recently, the livestock breeder had to rely solely upon his skill but nowadays the successful breeder of any animal needs, amongst other skills, at least some knowledge of the workings of heredity if he is to stand any chance of equalling, let alone beating, his competitors.

To understand the principles of scientific rabbit breeding, to improve stock and to attempt to unravel the origins of the modern breeds, it is necessary to appreciate the manner in which genetic information is passed from one generation to the next.

LAWS OF INHERITANCE

Inheritance in all plants and animals is governed by two laws originally discovered by an Austrian monk, Gregor Mendel. The First Law of Inheritance tells us that the individual units (*genes*), which carry the inherited characteristics on to the next generation, exist in the offspring in pairs, made up of one gene from each parent. The genes retain their identity from one generation to the next.

The Second Law of Inheritance, also known as the Law of Independent Assortment, tells us that, during the formation of the reproductive cells, each pair of genes separates independently of every other pair of genes.

Together these rules mean that the rabbit may possess characteristics which originally came from either the mother or the father and that these characteristics will be independent of each other.

To apply these scientific laws to the rabbit, it is necessary to realise that the animal's body consists of millions of cells, each adapted to perform specific roles within the body. Yet, although these cells are completely different, they all contain the same genetic information. Common to the structure of all cells is the nucleus and, situated within the nucleus, are forty-four thread-like *chromosomes* grouped together in twenty-two pairs.

The chromosomes are built up of the basic units of inheritance, the genes, and each gene is allocated its own place (termed the *locus*) on a particular chromosome. In the rabbit, each pair of chromosomes consists of one gene collection derived from the buck and one from the doe. In some instances more than one alternative gene can occupy the same locus and these variants are responsible for the different characteristics that give rise to mutations. The alternative genes that can occupy the same locus are referred to as *alleles*. Where each parent contributes the same allele then the genes of each pair governing the particular activity will be identical and the rabbit is described as being *homozygous* with respect to the particular gene: the pair of genes themselves are called the *diploid* pair. If the members of the diploid pair are different then the rabbit is said to be heterozygous. Of the many different diploid pairs, any animal will be homozygous for some factors and heterozygous for others. The First Law of Inheritance states that both genes retain their identity. However, often one gene is *dominant* to another and, although the unseen gene remains as a *recessive*, to reappear in future generations, from a visual examination of the animal it would seem that the only gene present is the dominant one whose effects can be seen. In some instances one allele is not totally dominant over the other and the two may even act together (blending inheritance) to produce an effect different from either of the pure genes.

Genes are conventionally referred to by italic letters. Dominant genes are shown by an upper case letter (*G*) and recessive genes by a lower case (*g*). At any particular locus for which there are two alleles, three gene pairs are possible:

1 *GG* in which the rabbit is homozygous with respect to the gene *G* and will display the characteristic of this gene.

2 *Gg* in which the rabbit is heterozygous and will usually display only the characteristics of the dominant gene *G*, although it may show a combined effect intermediate between the two alleles, as in the case of English spotting (*Enen*).

3 *gg* where the rabbit is seen as a recessive with respect to that gene.

Genes are involved in all aspects of the rabbit's life, including the construction of the body, behavioural features such as nest-building and the inheritance of coat characteristics; the latter has been extensively investigated.

INHERITANCE IN THE NEW INDIVIDUAL

In order to understand the Second Law of Inheritance, it is necessary to know how *gametes* (reproductive cells) are formed. New cells are formed continuously throughout the life of the animal by a process called *mitosis*

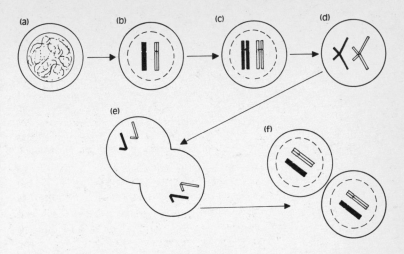

Fig. 14. Mitotic division of a cell. Interphase (a) in which the cell is not undergoing any reproductive process. Reproduction commences (b) with the disappearance of the nuclear membrane. Both chromosomes of the pair duplicate (c) but the two parts remain attached at the centromere (d). The chromatids begin to pull apart (e) and move to opposite ends of the cytoplasm – the non-nuclear material. The nuclear membrane reforms and two new daughter cells, similar in every respect to the parent cell, result (f).

(Fig. 14). In mitosis, there is first a breakdown of the membrane of the nucleus, after which the paired chromosomes split to form *chromatids* (fibres from which the new chromosomes will form). At this stage the fibres are held together at a point called the *centromere*. The chromatids then pull apart and begin to move to opposite ends of the enlarged cells forming the two daughter nuclei of the new cells and the cell divides. The two daughter cells contain chromosomes identical to those of the parent cell and are also identical in every other respect.

Cell division in the testes and the ovaries occurs by a different mechanism – *meiosis* (Fig. 15). Chromatids form in the normal manner, but each chromatid then aligns itself with its partner, i.e. the chromatid derived from the chromosome of the other parent. The chromatids now cross over and exchange partners. The crossover can occur at any point along the chromatids and it is possible for several crossovers and exchange of parts to take place. The result is that two new cells with paired chromosomes are formed purely as a result of random selection. Genes in close proximity to each other are less likely to be separated during the splitting process, and will tend to stay together. The frequency with which particular genes separate indicates their relative position on the chromosome and this has allowed scientists to investigate further the structure of genetic material.

Each reproductive cell will be different from every other and each cell will be capable of passing on both dominant and recessive genes; moreover, the equivalent of one gene of each diploid pair of the parents will be completely

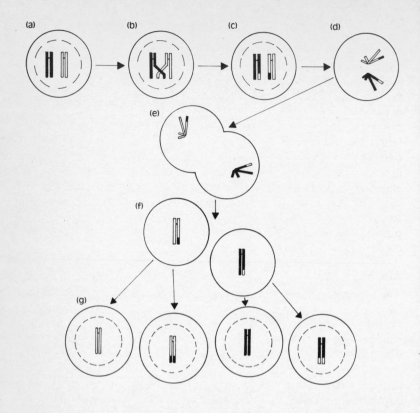

Fig. 15. Meiotic division of a cell (the formation of reproductive cells or gametes). The pair of chromatids making up the chromosome (a) begin a crossover process in which part of one chromosome is exchanged for part of the other one (b and c). The chromosomes separate (d and e) and two daughter cells result (f), which are different both from each other and from the parent cell. Each now undergoes a second division in which the chromatids split into two and each duplicates as in mitotic division. The result is four cells, all different from each other (g).

lost. It is often thought that siblings, if mated, will pass on similar characteristics to the young. This is not so. A rabbit which is a winner will gain prizes because the genetic factors that are required are dominant. In an animal in which they are not apparent it is highly probable that they have been lost in the inheritance process. Whilst it is often said that inferior animals may breed winners, this widely held belief does not stand up to scientific investigation. The rule for improvement of stock is always breed best to best. Large amounts of money should not be paid for an animal simply because its brother is a champion. Where the stock originates from a stud which consistently produces winners, the breeder will have probably been using scientific selection methods and the line will have become homozygous for the necessary features, which will be apparent in the majority of kittens in the litter. It is these youngsters that must be sought.

COAT COLOUR

The factors which make up a particular breed or variety of rabbit are: coat colour, pattern, distribution of colour within the hair, distribution of marked hairs, spotting and body type. The colour and pattern of the rabbit (excluding spotting and silvering) are controlled by five gene loci on the chromosomes. The natural coat, i.e. the one containing the greatest number of dominant genes (otherwise it will not remain the preferred pattern) and devoid of mutations, may be taken as the starting point for considering the factors involved in pelt pigmentation. The wild coat is made up of two basic colouring materials or pigments, eumelanin (black-brown) and phaeomelanin (beige), together with colour modifiers and enhancers. No other colours are known. Blue is the result of dilution of black pigmentation and is not due to a distinct chemical. Likewise, lilac is a dilution of the chocolate-brown (which in turn is the non-development of the black pigment) shade. All of the colour shades known are the result of the action of the five major genes under consideration.

AGOUTI COAT

The wild or Agouti coat consists of three hair types: the fur fabric, which is slate-blue at the base with a yellow layer above it; secondary guard hairs with similar colour markings; primary guard hairs which possess the same banding but are tipped with black, giving an all-over three-band appearance. The Agouti belly is lighter in appearance due to the partial or total absence

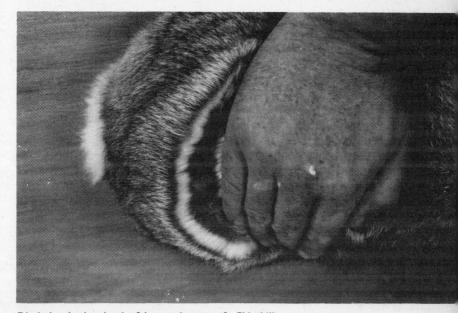

Displaying the three bands of the agouti pattern of a Chinchilla.

71

of the black-tipped primary guard hairs. The more important genes responsible for the colour pattern are denoted by letters of the alphabet and the alleles of a particular locus are termed a *series*.

A Series

This is concerned with the distribution of pigment within the individual hairs (which produces the banding) and the variety of marking of hairs in different positions on the body, e.g. Agouti rabbits have all-black eyebrows and lacing to the ears. The series is:

A	Agouti
a^t	Tan
a	Self

Where the dominant A gene is present the pattern will be as described above. The Tan pattern consists of a single colour covering the back of the animal, except for a triangle with its base at the base of the ears and its apex towards the tail. There are light markings around the eyes, the chest and down the sides, extending under the belly. The whole effect is that of a two-coloured rabbit, the pigmentation being the same from the tip to the base in any particular hair. With selection over the years, the Tan pattern has been modified and features such as pea spots (the small round dots on the face of the rabbit) have been emphasised. The Tan pattern has been used to breed other fancy varieties, such as Foxes and Martens, as well as the less common Otters. The recessive a is present in all single-colour (self) rabbits, although it may be absent from those animals carrying the genes for albinism. The gene allows for only one colour in all three hair types, although the intensity of the colour does tend to decrease near to the skin. This reflects the reduction in the amount of pigment in the hair follicle as the growth cycle reaches its conclusion. Colour extending to the base of the hair will be the result of good genetic composition, good husbandry and good nutrition. As a consequence, it is much sought after in the exhibition rabbit and no animal should be considered a good specimen unless the pigment extends to the base of the hair shaft.

B Series

This series is concerned with the development of the black colour within the hair. Where the totally dominant B is present then normal colour results, but the effect of the recessive b is to stop the development of the black colour, allowing the hairs to appear chocolate in colour. The actual shade can vary quite considerably as a result of the modifiers present – from a light milk-chocolate shade through to the deep hue of the Havana. The series is:

B	Development of black
b	Non-development of black

C Series

This series consists of five alleles which range in their action from total development of colour through to no colour at all (albinoism). The Chinchilla alleles stop the development of colour by first arresting the deposition of the yellow shade. Going down the series, the development of black becomes progressively more difficult. It is seen next as a sepia shade in the Sables, through to only the nose, feet, ears and tail being coloured in the Himalayan, until no colour at all is developed in the Albino, not even in the eye (which is red – as it is in the Himalayan). The series is:

C	Full colour
c^{chd}	Dark Chinchilla
c^{chm}	Medium Chinchilla
c^{chl}	Light Chinchilla
c^h	Himalayan
c	Albino

Apart from C, which is totally dominant over all the other alleles, incomplete dominance is exhibited by the other genes. Which gene pair is best in such breeds as the Chinchilla is still a matter of debate whilst, in other breeds, such as the Smoke Pearls and Sables, a heterozygous diploid pair is often deliberately sought.

Interaction of two genes in the middle of the series can have the most profound effect on the final appearance of the pelts. This makes it impossible to predict with any degree of certainty the result of a particular cross and the interpretation of the genetic composition based upon appearance alone is impossible.

The Dark Chinchilla allele inhibits development of yellow and the exhibition Chinchilla is an Agouti in which the banding is white (pearl) instead of the yellow shade of the wild ancestor. It is in the Light Chinchilla that the tendency to produce a sepia colour manifests itself. This reluctance to allow the formation of pigment can also be seen in the eyes, which change from blue through brown, shades of ruby and finally pink.

With the Light Chinchilla, there is a tendency for the extremities to be darker in colour than the body. This is most noticeable in the Himalayan pattern, which has been shown to be temperature-dependent. If hair is shaved from the white portion of a Himalayan, when the new hair emerges it will be coloured, the pigment having been deposited within the medulla of the hair as a result of the lowering of the temperature. The extremities, which are coloured in the Himalayan, would be at a slightly lower temperature than other parts of the body. The appearance of yellow in the back of the Himalayan is probably due to the presence of colour intensifiers and is not an inherent part of the pattern. As a consequence it should be possible to breed out the fault. Because of the temperature dependence, every effort should be made to keep Himalayans, and also those breeds such as Sables which are close to it in the genetic series, at as even a temperature as possible. They should not be housed outside.

If a rabbit has aa at its Agouti locus, then, in the presence of only one C gene, it will be a black rabbit. If the rabbit has the genes cc, no colour will occur in the eye or the fur, irrespective of whatever other genes are present. Even if the colour markings themselves are dominant, they will not be able to influence the pattern of the pelt if the factor for albinoism is present.

D Series

The dilution series (*D*) is concerned with the density of the pigment deposited in the hairs. Normal density occurs when the totally dominant gene *D* is present. When this is replaced with *dd*, far less pigment is deposited in the hair shaft. This allows more light to pass through and it appears as a lighter shade. Where a rabbit has *Dd* in its make-up, it is impossible, with the naked eye, to detect any difference from *DD*. The series is:

D   Normal density of pigment
d   Dilute density of pigment

E Series

Termed the extension-of-black series, this collection of genes is responsible for the distribution of black throughout the hairs of the rabbit. It will influence both aspects of the Agouti pattern, i.e. the banding and distribution of black hairs throughout the body of the rabbit. The series is:

E^d Dominant black, which is an increase of black, even to the Self shade, at the expense of the yellow of the Normal Agouti pattern

E   Normal extension of black as found in the Agouti and described above

e^j Japanese brindling, in which the black pigment appears in only some of the hairs while the others remain totally yellow

e   Total elimination of the black pigment. A fifth gene, E^s, which is dominant, lying between E^d and E, has been suggested; if it does exist it is almost impossible for anyone other than a geneticist to distinguish between the effects of E^d and E^s and the modifying influence of the presence or absence of intensfiers. For simplicity further discussion of this possible allele will be omitted.

Dominant black, despite its name, is not totally dominant over the normal extension. Together with the normal extension, it is responsible for the steel colour ($E^d E$) in which not only are the individual hairs modified but the belly fur has a greater extension of colour so that the pelt has the appearance of one all-over colour, similar to a Self. If E^s is accepted then steel grey is $E^s E$.

The E^d gene, because it is highest in the series, might be expected to be the preferred form in the wild rabbit. It is almost certain that the mutation would have occurred in wild populations but it is more likely that the reverse is true, i.e. the normal extension *E* was the mutation and the governing factor was the coat pattern offering the greatest camouflage and protection. A rabbit with total extension would be easier for a predator to see and the white colour of the tail present in the *E* form, but not in E^d, would be the part that airborne predators, such as eagles, would home in on. This would act as a protective mechanism because the talons of the attacking bird would tend to miss the body of the animal and not be able to get a grip on the pliable tail. Nevertheless, E^dE^d are almost certainly the genes present in the melanistic varieties which have emerged on islands where predators are fewer than usual, especially if they had been killed prior to rabbit-farming, and the protection aspects are no longer so important. Here the evolution of the rabbit would have been governed by the greatest dominance of genes rather than by natural selection for other features. The increase in the extension of black is at the expense of the yellow of the Agouti pattern.

Japanese brindling is probably the most startling of all the mutations of the rabbit, producing, as it can with selection, alternating black and yellow patterns to the extent that one cheek is yellow and the other almost black. In the Tricolour Dutch, the ears are the opposite shade to the cheeks. The yellow shade is the result of virtual non-extension of black, whilst the dark colour corresponds to almost total extension. This gene is responsible for the alternating patterns of the Harlequins and Magpies, as well as the two-tone effects seen in the Rhinelander.

The total elimination of the black pigment occurs with *ee* which is recessive to other alleles of the series. The rabbit is an orange-yellow or beige colour, depending on the colour intensifiers present.

While *ee* results in the total elimination of the black in the Agouti pattern, in the presence of the Self pattern some bluish-black markings remain on the flanks, cheeks and in certain other positions. This colour is referred to as either Tortoiseshell or Sooty Fawn, depending on the breed being discussed.

VARIATIONS IN FUR TYPE

There are four major genes which need to be considered in explaining the majority of variations in coat type; two are concerned with length, one with thickness of the individual hairs, and a less common gene concerned with waviness of the hair.

L Series (Angoras)

The coat of the English Angora consists almost entirely of fur fabric and secondary guard hairs, the primaries having been almost entirely eliminated. This is the result of selection rather than the action of the Angora gene. In the French Angora, with its altogether coarser coat, there are far more primary hairs present. Although these two breeds are quite distinct in some aspects, and the French breed lacks the furnishings of the English equivalent, the overall Angora effect is due to the same gene (*l*) which is recessive to the normal *L*.

The hair follicle which produces the shaft has a cyclic growth pattern. No hair in any animal grows continuously but, instead, the hair follicle produces hair for a certain period of time, then undergoes a rest period before entering a new growth phase. As the new hair emerges, it pushes out the old hair shaft. It is these old shafts which can be collected and spun into wool. With the Angora mutation, the growth period is longer than in other

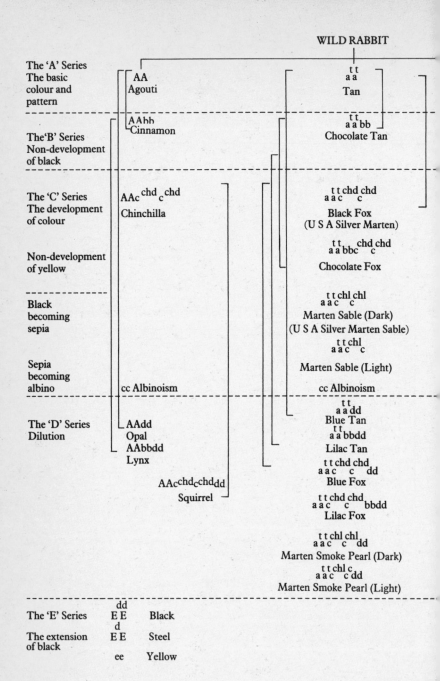

WILD RABBIT

The 'A' Series
The basic
colour and
pattern

$$\begin{matrix} & AA \\ & Agouti \end{matrix}$$

$$\begin{matrix} t\,t \\ a\,a \\ Tan \end{matrix}$$

The 'B' Series
Non-development
of black

$$\begin{matrix} A\,A\,h\,h \\ Cinnamon \end{matrix}$$

$$\begin{matrix} t\,t \\ a\,a\,b\,b \\ Chocolate\ Tan \end{matrix}$$

The 'C' Series
The development
of colour

$$AAc^{chd}c^{chd}$$
Chinchilla

$$\begin{matrix} t\,t\,c^{chd}c^{chd} \\ a\,a\,c \\ Black\ Fox \\ (U\,S\,A\ Silver\ Marten) \end{matrix}$$

**Non-development
of yellow**

$$\begin{matrix} t\,t \\ a\,a\,b\,b\,c \end{matrix}c^{chd}c^{chd}$$
Chocolate Fox

**Black
becoming
sepia**

$$\begin{matrix} t\,t\,c^{chl}c^{chl} \\ a\,a\,c \\ Marten\ Sable\ (Dark) \\ (U\,S\,A\ Silver\ Marten\ Sable) \end{matrix}$$

$$\begin{matrix} t\,t\,c^{chl} \\ a\,a\,c \end{matrix}c$$

**Sepia
becoming
albino**

cc Albinoism

Marten Sable (Light)

cc Albinoism

The 'D' Series
Dilution

AAdd
Opal
AAbbdd
Lynx

$$\begin{matrix} t\,t \\ a\,a\,d\,d \\ Blue\ Tan \end{matrix}$$

$$\begin{matrix} t\,t \\ a\,a\,b\,b\,d\,d \\ Lilac\ Tan \end{matrix}$$

$$AAc_c{chd}{chd}dd$$
Squirrel

$$\begin{matrix} t\,t\,c^{chd}c^{chd} \\ a\,a\,c\ \ c\ \ d\,d \\ Blue\ Fox \end{matrix}$$

$$\begin{matrix} t\,t\,c^{chd}c^{chd} \\ a\,a\,c\ \ c\ \ b\,b\,d\,d \\ Lilac\ Fox \end{matrix}$$

$$\begin{matrix} t\,t\,c^{chl}c^{chl} \\ a\,a\,c\ \ c\ \ d\,d \end{matrix}$$
Marten Smoke Pearl (Dark)

$$\begin{matrix} t\,t\,c^{chl}c \\ a\,a\,c\ \ c\,d\,d \end{matrix}$$
Marten Smoke Pearl (Light)

The 'E' Series
The extension
of black

$$\begin{matrix} dd \\ E\,E \\ d \\ E\,E \\ ee \end{matrix}$$

Black

Steel

Yellow

NOTE: Where two or more genotypes are possible
the homozygous system has been given

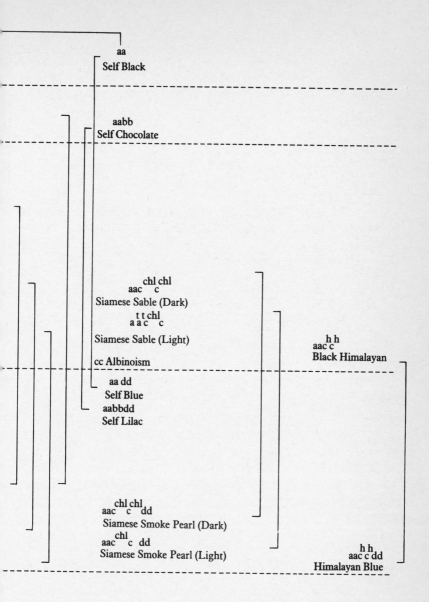

breeds. The usefulness of the hair has led to the Angora being one of the most highly developed of all rabbits. It is available in Self colours as well as in Chinchillated forms, but all colours and patterns are possible.

The Angora mutation appears in other breeds, such as the Swiss Fox. These have longer hair than the normal breeds but not as long as exhibition Angoras; the latter have been bred selectively for very long hair in the same way as Lops were bred for their ears. The absence of any trace of furnishings in these breeds suggests that these may be due to the presence of a secondary gene which has been bred into the English Angoras.

R Series (Rexes)

All three types of hair (fur fabric, primary and secondary guard hairs) are present in the Rex mutation but the guard hairs have been greatly reduced in length, as have the smellers. It is often incorrectly thought that there are no guard hairs in good Rexes because of the appearance from time to time of guard hairs protruding above the level of the pelt in poor specimens and it is mistakenly believed that the true Rex is the result of breeding out the guard hairs. This is not the case. The guard hairs have simply been reduced in length and an examination of the skin will reveal their presence. Those which protrude must be removed by selective breeding in the same way that other faults are corrected.

There are three different Rex mutations which give broadly the same effect and the rabbits that result are referred to as Normandy, German and French Rexes. They should not be crossbred as any hybrid will be vastly inferior to a pure Rex. However there is very little likelihood of crossing happening today as only French Rexes are bred. The Abbé Gillet, a French priest, obtained a mutant Rex rabbit which occurred amongst the stock of one of the local farmers and, from this, he bred a short-coated Agouti Rex which he called a Castor Rex. Translated this means 'the King of the Beavers' as its fur appeared to have a close resemblance to the much sought-after beaver fur. Rexes were soon bred in a whole range of colours and they attained a degree of popularity which has never diminished. As with all mutations, very careful selection was necessary to bring the stock up to the standard of today's Rexes.

The single gene responsible for the Rex mutation is r (sometimes written as r_1 to distinguish it from the German and Normandy mutations). It is totally recessive to the normal R.

Wa Series (Wavy Coat)

The wavy coat mutation appears to manifest itself only in the presence of the recessive gene (r). When combined with r, it gives rise to the Astrex. The wavy coat variety is not very popular with the Fancy.

Sa Series (Satins)

The Satin mutation leads to a very much finer hair shaft than that of the normal pelt, resulting in the most exquisitely soft coat. It is the result of the single mutant gene (*sa*), fully recessive to the normal *Sa*. The colour of rabbits containing this mutation may be different from that of the Normal as a result of the light being refracted in a different manner. The Albino Satin (*ccsasa*) is referred to not as a White, but as an Ivory Satin, which is a better description of the appearance of the variety.

Experiments have shown that it is possible to combine the Rex with the Angora, as well as both types with the Satin. At the moment, the only cross to have been developed by the Fancy is the Satin Rex (*rrsasa*).

SPOTTED RABBITS

There is a range of marked rabbits, which is the result not of colour spotting but rather of genes that confer varying amounts of white onto a Self background. If this were not the case, the coloured spots could be superimposed onto any other colour. The fact that, wherever spotting is observed, one of the colours is always white establishes that it is this colour which the gene is conferring on the pelt. Moreover the position of the white is the same irrespective of any other colour involved. If these were white rabbits with coloured markings, then they would be expected to have pink eyes, a feature never found in any spotted rabbits. All spotted varieties are thought to be the result of just three gene series.

Du Series (Dutch Spotting)

The exact number or form of the alleles of the *Du* gene are not known and there is more than one theory to explain the occurrence of the Dutch pattern. There is a dominant gene (*Du*) which, when present, will ensure that the rabbit has none or very few white markings. The recessive alleles du^w and du^d bestow greater and lesser degrees of white spotting. Of more importance to the breeder are the genes that work in combination with the major pattern-producing factor to afford the desired effects on the various parts of the body. The major problem with the Dutch rabbit is that two apparently very well-marked rabbits can be mated together and will produce young far removed from the desired pattern. Such results occur with all breeds, but it is so common with the Dutch as to suggest that there may be several genes working together. Also, the ease with which the genes separate suggests that they are not all situated closely together on just one chromosome. It is the complexity of the genetics that makes the Dutch such a challenge to breed.

En Series (English Spotting)

At the locus responsible for English spotting in the wild rabbit lies the semi-recessive *en* gene; a mutant semi-dominant *En* is also known. The English, or Butterfly as it is sometimes called (because of the shape of the smut on the nose), is the result of a heterozygous system in which the two genes work together rather than one being totally dominant over the other. Where a rabbit has the *enen* configuration, it will possess more coloured markings and the rabbits are known as Self. Such a gene would have been the preferred one within a warren and would have survived as it would appear to have few disadvantages for natural selection, whereas the *EnEn* system (in which the animal contains far more white spotting and is referred to as a Charlie) would have provided less camouflage.

By mating Selfs to Charlies, 100 per cent of the young should carry the English pattern. However, it is not only the basic pattern that is required but also the correct-sized marking in the right position. In order to obtain specimens with the ideal butterfly, herring-bone, chain and teat spots, it is far better to mate English (*Enen*) to English (*Enen*). This will result in 25 per cent each of Selfs and Charlies and 50 per cent English. These will be closer to their parents than the alternative cross which has only the grandparents as a guide to the outcome of particular matings.

Some breeds, notably the Lops, are bred extensively in the broken pattern and this probably has the same main genetic composition as the English. A comparison of the two illustrates the importance of selection in establishing a breed standard. Although the pattern is not so demanding as that of the English, the same breeding principles can be adopted.

Dutch and English genes are additive in their action. Where both are present, the resultant rabbit usually has far more white colour than either of the parents.

With selection, the most important factor in the breeding of spotted varieties, it is possible to produce a variety in which almost all the colour is removed from the Self black rabbit, from which it may be considered to have been derived. All that remains is a black ring around the eyes, black eyelashes and the brown colour of the eyes.

This is almost certainly the origin of the Blanc de Hotot. Although the rabbit is only shown as a black, there is no genetical reason why other colours should not be developed. All that would be required is to cross Dutch with English and continue selecting. The required variety is thought to be --*EnEndudu*, where -- represents the genes necessary to produce the primary colour. The better approach to creating new colours would be to start with a Blanc de Hotot and a Self of the required colour of as near to the correct type as it was possible to obtain. Each animal used in the breeding programme would have to be very carefully examined and its genotype worked out as far as practical from its appearance, in order to avoid breeding several wasted generations.

Both English and Dutch patterns occur in other breeds. The American Checkered Giant, the Dalmation Rex and the Rhinelander all contain English spotting. The Continental European Babroçon is a Dutch with far less white spotting than the more commonly bred form of the mutation.

V Series (Viennese White)

A third, complete-spotting, gene, the Viennese White, exists in which the entire coat is white. It is not an Albino (totally devoid of pigment), as pigment is developed in the iris of the eye, which is blue, establishing that the capacity to produce colour still exists. This gene has led to the development of the Blue-Eyed Whites which are perhaps best known as the Dwarfs and the Polish. The mutant gene responsible for the effect (v) is recessive to V which is present in the wild-type coat.

W Series (Wide Band)

A recessive gene (w) is known which widens the yellow band of the Agouti pattern. This can result in a yellow band of half or more of the total length of the hair and, with selection, can give rise to beige-coloured rabbits. In the modified Agouti, this wide band may still be seen. The Chinchilla frequently affords 'ghosts' in the litters as a result of the wide band greatly increasing the length of the pearling until it dominates the pelt colour. Wide band may be responsible for the colour in British New Zealand Reds and Belgian Hares. The effect of intensifiers can result in the colour varying from fawn to mahogany.

Silvering

In so far as silvering is passed from one generation to the next, and the characteristic can be transferred from one colour to another, it is genetic in its action. However, it may not be due simply to one major gene, as are the other effects, but is rather the result of selecting those specimens which have the greater number of white hairs in the pelt. The result would be the creation of a sport, the result of several factors rather than just one, as in the case of the pure single mutations. (There would have been sufficient incentive over the years to create such white speckled coats as the early specimens, the sports, would have commanded the highest prices from the fashion-conscious nobility.) This view is supported by the fact that it is possible to obtain all densities of silvering. Interpretation is further complicated by the two types of silvers: the English Silvers and the French Argentes, with rather more white hairs. For purposes of interpretation, it is usually taken that one recessive mutant, given the symbol si, is responsible for the effect.

OTHER FACTORS

TWO OR MORE MUTANTS

Some of our modern breeds depend upon only one mutant gene for their pelt colour and markings, but many are the result of more than one mutant gene. An all-black rabbit simply differs in its markings from its wild counterpart in that the gene pair AA has been replaced with aa (or E^dE^d for EE). In the blue rabbit, the genes are the same as for the black, except that DD has been replaced with dd, thus involving two mutant systems. If a chocolate is crossed with a blue there are three mutant gene pairs ($aabbdd$). This gives the lilac which, in turn, can be Rexed, giving an overall pelt genotype of *aabbddrr*. For all practical purposes, this is the limit of the number of mutants which can be dealt with in one animal. Spotting could be incorporated, but the result may not be pleasing to the eye because of the difficulty of getting so many factors, such as pelt density and texture, as well as type, correct. It could not be bred sufficiently close to its standard to have a realistic chance of winning in the Duplicate classes.

PARTIALLY DOMINANT GENES

With the exception of those of the English and Dutch, all the genes previously discussed are either totally dominant or totally recessive and behave independently of their partner in the diploid pair. However, when two alleles of the C series act together, they can produce some unpredictable effects.

Sables and Smoke Pearls are both the result of Chinchilla mutations giving rise to the non-development of yellow. Both are split into Siamese, which is the Self pattern, and Marten, which has the characteristic distribution associated with the Tan pattern. Sables are the full colour whilst Smoke Pearls contain the dilution factor. The situation is further complicated when one of the c^{chl} genes is replaced with c^h (Himalayan) or c (Albino). The genes $c^{chl}c^{chl}$ afford the dark version of the variety, $c^{chl}c^h$ gives the medium shade and $c^{chl}c$ yields the palest or light form. What

Table 4

Genotypes which may be obtained by crossing various shades of Sable (crossings within the mid to lower Chinchilla series)

1 Dark Sable × Medium Sable   2 Dark Sable × Light Sable
    ($c^{chl}c^{chl}$)   ($c^{chl}c^h$)   ($c^{chl}c^{chl}$)   ($c^{chl}c$)

	Dark Sable c^{chl}	Dark Sable c^{chl}		Dark Sable c^{chl}	Dark Sable c^{chl}
Medium Sable c^{chl}	$c^{chl}c^{chl}$ (Dark Sable)	$c^{chl}c^{chl}$ (Dark Sable)	Light Sable c^{chl}	$c^{chl}c^{chl}$ (Dark Sable)	$c^{chl}c^{chl}$ (Dark Sable)
c^h	$c^{chl}c^h$ (Medium Sable)	$c^{chl}c^h$ (Medium Sable)	c	$c^{chl}c$ (Light Sable)	$c^{chl}c$ (Light Sable)

3 Medium Sable × Medium Sable
($_c$chl$_c$) ($_c$chl$_c$h)

Medium Sable

	$_c$chl	$_c$h
Medium Sable $_c$chl	$_c$chl$_c$chl (Dark Sable)	$_c$chl$_c$h (Medium Sable)
$_c$h	$_c$chl$_c$h (Medium Sable)	$_c$h$_c$h (Himalayan)

4 Light Sable × Light Sable
($_c$chl$_c$) ($_c$chl$_c$)

Light Sable

	$_c$chl	$_c$
Light Sable $_c$chl	$_c$chl$_c$chl (Dark Sable)	$_c$chl$_c$ (Light Sable)
$_c$	$_c$chl$_c$ (Light Sable)	$_c$c (Albino)

5 Medium Sable × Light Sable
($_c$chl$_c$h) ($_c$chl$_c$)

Medium Sable

	$_c$chl	$_c$h
Light Sable $_c$chl	$_c$chl$_c$chl (Dark Sable)	$_c$chl$_c$h (Medium Sable)
$_c$	$_c$chl$_c$ (Light Sable)	$_c$h$_c$ (White with some coloured points★)

★Result of incomplete dominance of $_c$h over c.

appears surprising is that, on occasions, mating two light forms of any of the four breeds can yield two light, one dark and one albino.

To account for this, and to predict the ratios of forms that will turn up in litters, a four-square grid can be used in the following way. Put the genes of the diploid pair contributed by the doe down the left-hand side and those contributed by the buck across the top. The genes that will be present in the young can be calculated as follows. Combine the first gene of the buck with the first gene of the doe and enter the pair obtained in the top left-hand square. Enter the first gene of the buck with the second gene of the doe in the bottom left-hand square, the second gene of the buck with the first of the doe in the top right-hand square and, finally, the second gene of the buck with the second of the doe in the remaining square. As an example, the results of replacing members of the *C* series in the Smoke Pearl and Sable varieties are shown in Table 4.

Genetic representation grids of this type may be drawn up for any number of variable genes. They are best employed to explain the results of particular matings rather than to predict what might appear within any one litter as the small number of young will be insufficient to yield the kittens in the exact statistical ratio. Moreover the fact that a particular colour or set of markings can result from a mating does not mean that all the resulting young would be of a type suitable for exhibition. In the above schemes one of the products could be a Himalayan; but it would only be a Himalayan in the sense that a Californian is a Himalayan; it would not possess the snaky body that is required to accompany the markings. This problem is eliminated when the colours are all superimposed onto a similar body type, such as in the Netherland Dwarf. A further complication arises in adopting a too theoretical approach to breeding; other factors such as colour intensifiers are involved in the production of the ideal exhibition animal and cross-coloured matings can involve the production of young of poor shades.

Medium sables may be, for example, $c^{chl}c^{chl}$ or $c^{chl}c^{h}$, depending upon the colour intensifiers present. The results obtained must therefore be treated with some caution.

In the Seal Point there are dark markings that approximate to the pattern of the Himalayan. These may be the result of gene combinations such as $c^{chm}c^{h}$ from very dark pointed specimens or $c^{chl}c^{h}$. Alternatively such markings can result from the genes for other sables with colour intensifiers. Whilst there may be no Himalayan genes as such present (since this mutation is temperature-dependent and the genes involved will almost certainly be near to it in the Chinchilla series) every effort must be made to ensure that such rabbits are not subjected to too large a temperature range. Certainly they should not be housed out of doors.

Genetic grids predict the likelihood of obtaining a particular colour combination. For example, the genotype for Tortoiseshell is *aaee*. To create a rabbit of this colour, a Black (*aaEE*) should be crossed with a Yellow (*AAee*) to give the F_1 hybrid *AaEe*. The grid for the F_2 hybrids (Table 5) shows only a one in sixteen chance of obtaining the desired combination, but it will be homozygous and breed true to colour.

Several genetic crosses are possible but only a few are of concern to the hobbyist. Table 6 shows the effect of crosses involving the most dominant and most recessive alleles in the *B*, *C* and *D* series and the gene for self. Together with the specialist tables given elsewhere in the text, Table 6 covers the majority of the more important crosses that the rabbit breeder will need to appreciate.

Table 5
Genotypes* obtained from mating F_1 hybrids obtained from crossing pure Black with pure Yellow

Genes contributed by buck
(AaEe)

Genes contributed by doe (AaEe)	*AE*	*Ae*	*aE*	*ae*
AE	*AAEE* (pure Agouti)	*AAEe*	*AaEE*	*AaEe*
Ae	*AAEe*	*AAee*	*AaEe*	*Aaee* (Yellow)
aE	*AaEE*	*AaEe*	*aaEE* (Self Agouti)	*aaEE* (Self Agouti)
ae	*AaEe*	*Aaee* (Yellow)	*aaEe* (Self Agouti)	*aaee* (Tortoiseshell or Sooty Fawn)

*All unmarked genotypes are impure Agoutis

The genes of the first four series for a Self black are *aaBBCCDD*. If a rabbit of this genotype were mated to an Albino carrying the genetic pattern for a lilac with the genotype *aabbccdd*, all the F_1 hybrids would contain *AaBbCcDd* genes. The effects of subsequent brother-to-sister matings would produce F_2 hybrids of the genotypes and colours displayed in Table 6.

Table 6 Genotypes and colours of F$_2$ hybrids from an original *aaBBCCDD* cross to *aabbccdd*

Genes (Contributed) By Doe	*Genes Contributed By Buck*							
	aBCD	*abCD*	*abcD*	*aBCd*	*aBcD*	*aBcd*	*abCd*	*abcd*
aBCD	*aaBBCCDD* (Black)	*aaBbCCDD* (Black)	*aaBbCcDD* (Black)	*aaBBCCDd* (Black)	*aaBBCcDD* (Black)	*aaBBCcDd* (Black)	*aaBbCCDd* (Black)	*aaBbCcDd* (Black)
abCD	*aaBbCCDD* (Black)	*aabbCCDD* (Chocolate)	*aabbCcDD* (Chocolate)	*aaBbCCDd* (Black)	*aaBbCcDD* (Black)	*aaBbCcDd* (Black)	*aabbCCDd* (Chocolate)	*aabbCcDd* (Chocolate)
abcD	*aaBbCcDD* (Black)	*aabbCcDD* (Chocolate)	*aabbccDD* (White)	*aaBbCcDd* (Black)	*aaBbccDD* (White)	*aaBbccDd* (White)	*aabbCcDd* (Chocolate)	*aabbccDd* (White)
aBCd	*aaBBCCDd* (Black)	*aaBbCCDd* (Black)	*aaBbCcDd* (Black)	*aaBBCCdd* (Blue)	*aaBBCcDd* (Black)	*aaBBCcdd* (Blue)	*aaBbCCdd* (Blue)	*aaBbCcdd* (Blue)
aBcD	*aaBBCcDD* (Black)	*aaBbCcDD* (Black)	*aaBbccDD* (White)	*aaBBCcDd* (Black)	*aaBBccDD* (White)	*aaBBccDd* (White)	*aaBbCcDd* (Black)	*aaBbccDd* (White)
aBcd	*aaBBCcDd* (Black)	*aaBbCcDd* (Black)	*aaBbccDd* (White)	*aaBBCcdd* (Blue)	*aaBBccDd* (White)	*aaBBccdd* (White)	*aaBbCcdd* (Blue)	*aaBbccdd* (White)
abCd	*aaBbCCDd* (Black)	*aabbCCDd* (Chocolate)	*aabbCcDd* (Chocolate)	*aaBbCCdd* (Blue)	*aaBbCcDd* (Black)	*aaBbCcdd* (Blue)	*aabbCCdd* (Lilac)	*aabbCcdd* (Lilac)
abcd	*aaBbCcDd* (Black)	*aabbCcDd* (Chocolate)	*aabbccDd* (White)	*aaBbCcdd* (Blue)	*aaBbccDd* (White)	*aaBbccdd* (White)	*aabbCcdd* (Lilac)	*aabbccdd* (White)

Note: if one *a* is replaced by A in the above scheme, all blacks become agoutis, all chocolates become cinnamons, all blues become opals and all lilacs become lynxes. If one *a* is replaced by *a*^{t}, all colours become corresponding tans, e.g. *a*^{t} – BbCcDd, which is a black and tan. Whites remain whites irrespective of other genes present.

COLOUR INTENSIFIERS

The basic colours are defined by the presence or absence of the major colour-conferring genes. However, in some instances, breed standards call for different shades, and even where they are not formally demanded some rabbits have vastly superior hues to others. How does this come about? As well as the primary colour genes, there are other hereditary factors which increase or decrease the quantities of pigment deposited in the hair shaft. These are similarly passed from generation to generation. Careful selection and the inclusion of other colours are the only practical way in which they can be established in a stud.

Intensity of colour is more readily seen in the dilute than in the dominant form. A dark blue may improve a black, but the improvement of blue to a darker shade will only result if the black carries the necessary intensifiers and it is impossible to detect these simply by observation. The presence of colour intensifiers can have such a profound effect on the colour that, in some instances, it is almost impossible to be sure of the main gene type without detailed examination. It is also possible that two different genes could be responsible for the colour in certain breeds where overlap of effects is possible. Only a very small percentage of the members of any breed have been examined. Within the sandy to mahogany range is an area where either *ee* or *ww* could be the main gene responsible for the colour. It is possible that, in different studs, the alternative to the normally quoted gene, together with the appropriate intensifiers, is the one that is responsible for the colour.

The yellow colour intensifier is of particular importance, its presence or absence having the most profound effect upon the pelt. Yellow colour developing in the Himalayan spoils the snow-white effect of the coat and, if present, vigorous selection must be adopted to remove it whereas, in certain Tan-derived breeds, such as the Otter, the presence of the yellow intensifier can result in a specimen possessing that extra brilliance that will make it into a flier.

Reference has already been made to the problems associated with spotted rabbits (p. 79) and again minor genes working in co-operation with the major pattern-bestowing factor are responsible for the finesse that produces a show-winner. The presence of these minor genes means that the only way to ensure a stud's continuing improvement is sound theory backed up by a vigorous selection programme.

PRACTICAL APPLICATIONS OF GENETICS

IN-BREEDING

In seeking to establish or improve a stud, it is necessary simultaneously to retain those features of the best rabbits and correct their weaknesses. It is a pointless waste of time to achieve one without the other. Where only minor improvements are required, or are even possible, then the most effective way of achieving this is by selection of better-quality stock of the same basic genetic composition as the original animals.

To maintain the genetic pattern and increase the homozygosity of the young, the technique of in-breeding, which can be used for selecting specific characteristics, may be employed. In-breeding consists of mating together closely related animals, such as brother to sister, or parent to offspring. Continuing the process for several generations means that the whole of a strain can be traced back to one main ancestor. As well as providing homozygosity for the desired characteristics it will also increase the occurrence of undesirable characteristics and any animals showing such tendencies must be ruthlessly culled.

Breeders tend to worry too much about the effects of close in-breeding. There is a gradual decrease in fertility and vigour but this tends to stabilise itself without further detriment. The best way to deal with the problem should it arise is to introduce an out-cross. It is possible to mate brother to sister for more than one generation, but the practice cannot be continued indefinitely. The exhibitor is only concerned with the flier, the individual that will win prizes, whereas the commercial rabbit-farmer will be seeking to maximise his yields, in terms of carcasses raised to marketable weight. He will find that out-crosses, possibly even as far as another breed, will be the best way of achieving his aims. Large whites such as New Zealands and Californians crossed to Dutch, itself not normally thought of as a meat rabbit, can produce good results. Where pelts as well as carcasses are important, two distinct strains of the same breed may be maintained to yield the breed stock. These are crossed to produce the marketable young.

GENE CONTRIBUTIONS IN IN-BREEDING

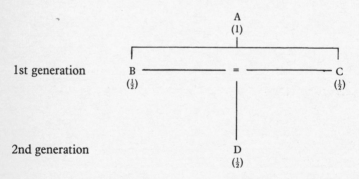

Note With a sib mating (full brother to sister) the resulting offspring will have a 50 per cent contribution from both the original buck and doe, although the second generation will have a distinctive genetic composition from the first, which will also have 50 per cent contribution from the original buck and doe.

LINE-BREEDING

Line-breeding involves less closely related stock than in-breeding, although it maintains the principle of retaining some related blood and a more gradual build-up of the homozygosity of the desired genes.

Frequently it is advantageous to use a system that incorporates some of the principles of in-breeding, such as brother-to-sister or father-to-daughter matings for one or two generations and then changing to line-breeding for a further two generations by incorporating matings of first or second cousins. In-breeding or line-breeding has become an obsession, with some breeders believing that it alone will solve their problems and simply advocating close-breeding for its own sake. Others feel the need to keep introducing out-crosses also for their own sake. Any system will only be as good as the animals which you are using. Whichever scheme you employ, always adjust so that you are involving your best animals rather than attempting to follow through a pre-arranged plan. It should be borne in mind that a far greater degree of close-breeding can be used than with other domestic animals such as cats and dogs, as factors such as temperament and mental behaviour are less important with the hutch-raised animal.

LINE-BREEDING (INTERMEDIATE BETWEEN IN-BREEDING AND OUT-CROSSING)

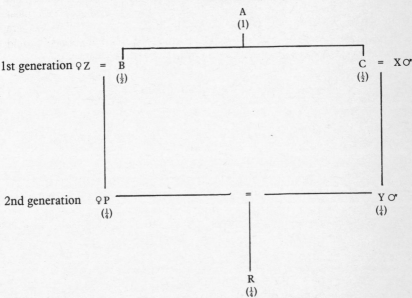

Note R has more of A's genes than would the corresponding generation using out-crossing. The offspring may be mated with one of A's line again, thus increasing the advantage of A's characteristics being inherited. It is possible to line-breed to more than one ancestor. X and Z are strangers.

LINE-BREEDING TO MORE THAN ONE LINE:
A PLAN FOR BREEDING FROM A TRIO OF ONE BUCK (A) AND TWO DOES (B AND C).

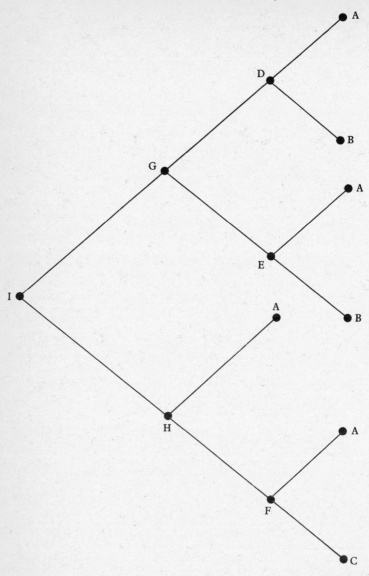

Note A is considered the best rabbit (buck), with B the better of the two does (B and C). Although there is a full brother-to-sister mating, no further line-breeding to B is involved because, by selection, better does should be obtained. The genetic make-up of I is: $\frac{5}{8}$A, $\frac{2}{8}$B and $\frac{1}{8}$C.

REPRESENTATION OF LINE-BREEDING BY TWO METHODS:
(a) A CONVENTIONAL PEDIGREE (b) A FLOW DIAGRAM

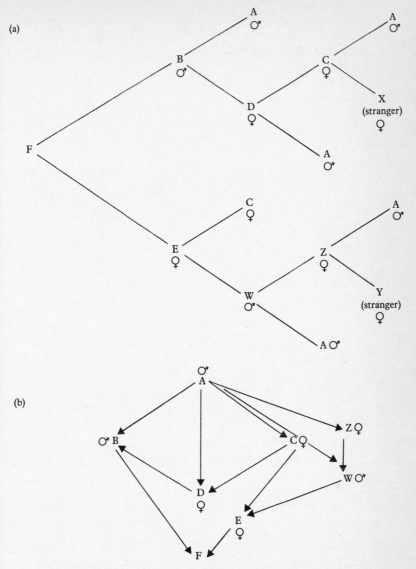

In both (a) and (b) buck A is mated with a stranger X to yield a doe C, which is then mated with A to give a doe D. D is then mated to her own grandfather A to give B. A is also mated to Y to give the doe Z, which is mated to A to give the buck W. W is mated with C a daughter of A to give E. E is mated with B to give F.

OUT-CROSSING

An out-cross is a mating to an animal that is not related to any of the rabbits in the stud. Such matings are from time to time included to introduce hybrid vigour and to improve certain characteristics that require the introduction of new genes. The causes of hybrid vigour have still not been fully explained but, when a completely new set of genes is introduced into any strain, the fertility is increased, as is the rate of growth in the individual. The results of such a mating will be seen in the first generation, but unless new blood is continually introduced there will be a gradual decline in the activity of the strain. Where a strain has been kept pure for generations and, in spite of the homozygosity of the majority of genes, one fault is still coming through, there will have been a corresponding build-up in the fault-causing gene to the state where it occurs with a frequency of almost 100 per cent. Further close-breeding will not eliminate the problem as there will be no opportunity to introduce the correcting gene. There will be virtually no chance of the required hereditary factor emerging of its own accord, as mutations only occur once in some hundreds of thousands of births.

Where the situation is reached in which an out-cross is necessary to correct these faults, very great care must be given to the selection of the individual. Select a buck that possesses all the characteristics which are lacking in your stock. Now select two proven does and set the three rabbits aside from the rest of your strain. Carefully examine the young which are obtained, not only for the hoped-for near-perfect specimens that could emerge from the first mating, but rather for the emergence of any major hereditary problems, such as bad eyes, either in the colour or health sense, and any white or other patches in the pelts. The purchased buck may be carrying as recessive genes serious faults which it would be disastrous to allow to enter your stock. One unfavourable out-cross will ruin all your years of careful breeding. Where such genes are suspected, the young, if they are healthy, must be disposed of by the usual method, any unhealthy youngsters must be culled, and the buck should be eliminated from the breeding programme and another male obtained from an alternative source. Any defects may be recessive and will not show up in the first generation. It is advisable to conduct a brother-to-sister mating and breed at least ten, preferably twenty, youngsters. Any recessive genes will show up in at least one of the kittens. Moreover, if the out-cross is going to work, there should be signs of improvement at this stage. Experimental out-crosses should be conducted in this way until the desired effect is obtained, but throughout the experiments it is essential to maintain the original strain in a pure form, so that it can be returned to until such time as it is deemed safe to include the out-cross or its progeny into the whole of the stud.

More common, and in some ways more difficult, is the need to include modifiers to improve colour, or one aspect of the coat pattern or the make-up of the rabbit. Since many of the genes work together and, in spite of their carrying their identity to the next generation according to the laws of genetics, it is often necessary to mate a rabbit deficient in one respect to another excessive with respect to that character. It appears in some instances that the more excessive the correction the greater the chance of success. The explanation may be that the two genes are working together synergistically. This does not follow in every instance, because of the different degrees of dominance exhibited by the various genes.

GENE CONTRIBUTIONS IN OUT-BREEDING

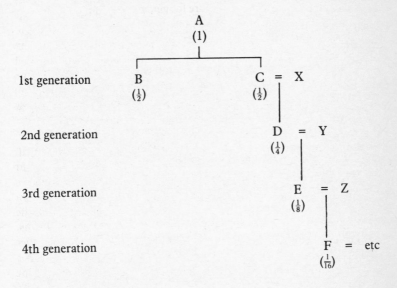

Note The fraction represents the amount of A's genetic contribution in later generations. X, Y and Z represent total strangers. With out-breeding in this way, the genetic contribution made by A halves in each successive generation.

RANDOM COLOUR BREEDING

Where a variety depends upon two different genes at the same locus to produce the colour, it is not possible to control the colour of the youngsters produced. Rather than being a disadvantage, this can be turned to the fancier's benefit. Dutch rabbits are one of the very few breeds in which it is possible to find examples of all the colours in the extension-of-black series. When two steel Dutch are mated together then up to four different colours (steel, black, pale grey and dark grey) will be obtained. This can be explained from a study of the gene grid below.

Quite considerable variations can be observed amongst the colour of steel

	E^d	E
E^d	E^dE^d (Black)	E^dE (Steel)
E	E^dE (Steel)	EE (Agouti – light or dark)

rabbits, due to the E^d gene and those genes which act in combination with it. In some instances, the blacks that result from steel crosses contain some Agouti hairs and are of no use for exhibition purposes. This is one of the strongest arguments for the presence of an E^s gene.

With dominant black, the black pigment extends not only throughout individual top hairs, but also to the hairs of the underside pattern; these are also coloured black. The resulting rabbit is indistinguishable from the more normal Self black, but has the genes AA rather than aa and E^dE^d instead of EE. Some believe that this is the finest black of all and it is claimed that many show-winners have been bred in this way. The specimen illustrated is AAE^dE^d rather than the more frequently encountered $aaEE$. It is highly unlikely that the shade of black produced by a different set of genes will not be different from the usual. Whether or not it is better, is a question of conjecture. It should also be pointed out that, occasionally, rabbits with brown-grey flanks appear in the litters and are of little use for showing. The steel-bred black Dutch may either be mated to an Agouti, to produce all-steels, a steel-bred black or a normal (aa) black. Not only can this alter the colour, but, by the latter crossing, the good points of Dutch spotting can be transferred from the steels to the blacks and *vice versa*, as both colours can appear in the subsequent litters.

The original true Self black could be either aa or if it were blue-bred $aadd$ crossed to a steel-bred black (AAE^dE^d). Such a mating would produce all-steels of genotype $AaDDE^dE$ or $AaDdE^dE$. To these alternatives, a third, that of the normal steel ($AADDE^dE$) must be considered when discussing the shade of the steel Dutch (the fourth genotype $AADdE^dE$ whilst being obtainable is unlikely to occur unless the self was blue black bred). Which yields the best colour is a question which will stimulate conversation at shows for years to come and will probably never be resolved; moreover, colour intensifiers will also have a profound effect upon the final shade.

The Agouti may be of a light or dark shade although the genotype is the same for both and the difference in colour is a result of intensifiers, the moderators that are also present. The percentage of light to dark may offer some insight into which ones are present in a particular strain. Incorporating a dark Agouti in a black Dutch breeding scheme may present another method of improving the colour. Before leaving the extension series and its relationship to the Dutch, the yellow is of genotype *ee* and the tortoiseshell (in many breeds termed the Sooty Fawn) is *aaee*, or a Self black-yellow (see page 55).

Perhaps with the Dutch, and its very exact demands on colour (more than most breeds), it is necessary to appreciate the complex genetics involved far more, but without the selection procedures it could well prove disappointing.

SELECTION

Selection has been used in breeding livestock since domestication began. It should not be considered as an alternative to scientific breeding but rather an important part of it. It is by selection that we effect the hereditary process by only breeding from those animals that have the desired characteristic. Selection is used to increase those factors that cannot be exactly defined, such as size. However, size itself is seldom dependent on simply a single factor but rather a whole range of features that serves to increase the size of the animal. The fancier will need to monitor a whole range of factors simultaneously: type, pelt, distribution of markings and exact colour. Selection, whether it be by culling or selling, should, where applicable, be from the earliest age and should continue into adulthood. The degree of selection will in the long term have more effect upon your stud than the initial quality of your stock or your knowledge of the scientific principles of breeding. Whilst any animal should be kept long enough to establish how good it really is, no offspring should ever be bred from unless it is an improvement on the parents. The rule must be: if in doubt, do not breed from the animal.

TESTING FOR GENETIC PURITY

Whilst some breeds are compounded of two or more colour factors as, for example, the Sables, Smoke Pearls and, in some cases, Dutch, in many varieties the reverse, genetic purity, is required if the strain is to progress. With new stock it is easy to establish whether a strain is pure with respect to any gene that is totally dominant over its alleles. This can be illustrated by considering the dilute gene *d* which is fully recessive to *D*, the allele for total deposition of colour. Where a rabbit is a Self black Rex it will not be apparent from an examination whether its genetic make-up is *aaDDrr* or *aaDdrr*, but a blue Rex can have only one genetic code (covering the genes under consideration), *aaddrr*. If the blue Rex is mated to the black then, providing that the black is pure, only black rabbits will be obtained whereas if it is impure then equal numbers of blacks and blues would be expected.

With small litters, the number is unlikely to be equal, because there will be insufficient young to produce the statistically correct ratio. But any appearance of blue rabbits will establish that the original animal was not pure with respect to the dilute gene.

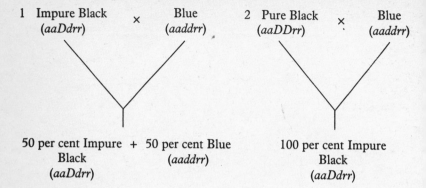

1 Impure Black   ×   Blue   2 Pure Black   ×   Blue
   (*aaDdrr*)   (*aaddrr*)   (*aaDDrr*)   (*aaddrr*)

50 per cent Impure + 50 per cent Blue   100 per cent Impure
    Black   (*aaddrr*)   Black
   (*aaDdrr*)   (*aaDdrr*)

OUT-CROSSING TO A DIFFERENT BREED OR VARIETY

It may be desirable, in order to improve the characteristics of one breed, to incorporate the genes from another breed as part of a long-term development scheme. This technique might be beneficially used for example where it is necessary to soften the hair by increasing the number of secondary to primary follicles, or, by reversing the process, to improve the resistance. Many years ago Angora genes were included in the make-up of many of our fur breeds, as evidenced by the occurrence of 'woollies' in today's litters. To increase the length of the hair of the fur rabbit, it is not the Angora gene itself that is required but the intensifiers which have been preferentially selected over the generations to increase the length of the Angora hair. These would help to improve the length of hair, but the occurrence of the recessive genes are thought by some breeders to negate the advantage.

Should you decide to conduct an out-cross, then such a breeding scheme should be conducted in parallel with the main programme. As soon as an animal emerges which appears to have the improved characteristics, it should be in-bred, if suitable other young emerge from the experimental breeding programme, for three generations and thereafter line-bred back to the improved rabbit's line. If only one worthwhile improvement emerges then this should be taken as A on p. 91 and the new breeding programme built up around it from the original strain which is being maintained in parallel.

CREATING A NEW VARIETY OR IMPROVING THE COLOUR

It may be extremely difficult to obtain certain varieties, or they may no longer be in existence. Any gene combination may be created, providing that you seek to add or improve only one factor at a time, that is, in a cross

96

Plate 1   New Zealand White (*cc*).

Plate 2   Angora (*ccll*).

Plate 3   Tortoiseshell English Lop (*aaee*).

Plate 4   Agouti French Lop.

Plate 5   Chinchilla Dwarf Lop (*$_cchd_cchd/m$*).

Plate 6   Blue Rex (*aaddrr*).

Plate 7   Black Rex (*aarr*).

Plate 8   Orange Rex (*eerr*).

Plate 9 Fawn Rex (*ddeerr*).

Plate 10 Sable Dwarf.

Plate 11 Smoke Pearl Dwarf.

Plate 12 Agouti Dwarf.

Plate 13 Dwarf Black Fox ($_aa_at_cchd_cchd$).

Plate 14   Polish Chocolate Fox ($a^t a^t bb c^{chd} c^{chd}$).

Plate 15   Chinchilla –Normal ($_cchd_cchd$).

Plate 16   Himalayan ($_{aa}c_hc_h$).

Plate 17   Belgian Hare (ww).

Plate 18   Black Tan (a_ta_t).

Plate 19 Black Fox – Normal ($a^t a^t c^{chd} c^{chd}$).

Plate 20   English (*aaEnen*).

Plate 21   Black Dutch (*E^dE^ddudu*) (N.B. *aadudu* would be visually similar.)

Plate 22   Steel Dutch (*E^dE dudu*).

Plate 23   Agouti Dutch (*dudu*).

Plate 24   Yellow Dutch (*eedudu*).

Plate 25   Silver (*aasisi*).

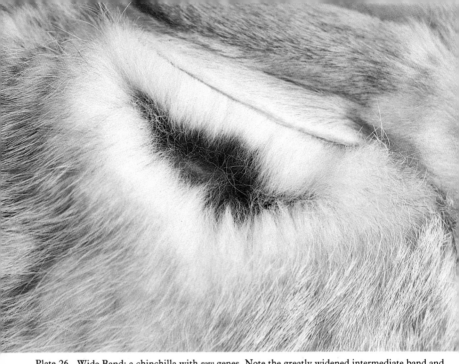

Plate 26 Wide Band: a chinchilla with *ww* genes. Note the greatly widened intermediate band and diminished slate blue base, compared with that of the dominant *W* gene. Such a chinchilla is known as a 'ghost'.

Plate 27 Chinchilla from the same litter as above with either *WW* or *Ww* genes – no wide band present. Note the single coloured hairs of the ear lacing, a feature of the Agouti gene *A*.

between two types, that originally present and the characteristic being introduced. Bear in mind that it is no good obtaining the correct pelt characteristics if the other factors such as type are wrong. Try, if at all possible, to create the new variety by starting with two animals of the desired breed. This will be possible with Rexes, Satins, Dwarfs and Poles. With other breeds, unless rabbits of the same or similar type are available, you must be prepared to wait several generations to obtain the desired body conformation together with the ideal pelt. This is the main reason why Dwarf and Polish displaying Dutch and English spotting have not been a success. Cross the two varieties. The first generation F_1 hybrids will not be homozygous and may not appear similar to the desired variety. The F_1 must now be bred brother to sister and the new variety will occur once in sixteen kittens as shown in Table 6 for AAee. This should serve as A in an inbreeding programme (see p. 88).

BLENDED GENES

Some varieties, such as the White (Ermine) Rex, have been bred to a far higher standard than others, such as the Castor Rex. Use can be made of the Ermine's superior coat characteristics to produce a top-quality Castor. The Castor Rex has all the genes of a normal Agouti plus the rexing genes rr.

Orange Rex, which have been similarly developed to a very high standard, contain all of the Agouti genes except EE, which is replaced by the recessive ee. Ermine Rex may contain any genes, providing that cc is present. If these two are mated together, then the Agouti genes of the Orange will be dominant, including the C for conferring colour. The E of the Ermine will dominate the e of the Orange, so that, if an Ermine Rex is mated to an Orange Rex, then the resultant young would be expected to be Castors (Agoutis) with the pelt texture of their two parents. A Castor bred in this way may well win more than a pure Rexed Agouti as the latter has not been bred sufficiently to reach the standard of many of the other Rexes. However such hybrids will not breed true and will certainly contribute nothing to the long-term improvement of the variety.

Adapting the technique, it is possible to run together three different-coloured varieties of the same breed. Where blues and chocolates are crossed in the F_1 generation, the litters will only contain blacks. Crossing of these in an in-breeding programme will result in blues, chocolates and lilacs which will all breed true, as well as blacks which may not. Blacks that are the result of half-chocolates or half-tortoiseshell do not have the same depth of colour as the homozygous specimens.

ADJACENT ALLELES

It cannot be ruled out that, with adjacent genes of the same series, such as a^t and a, or e^j and e, there could be some interaction similar to that described for the Chinchilla series and that, possibly, the young of mixed genes could be nearer to the breed standard than those of pure genetic make-up. Even if

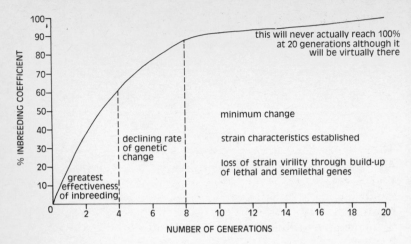

Fig. 16. Increasing the gene contribution of two ancestors as a result of continual inbreeding.

this were the case, there would be no advantage in creating a series of heterozygous rabbits that will never breed completely true, and the rule should be, where possible, always to seek and retain homozygosity.

However, this may not have happened in the past. If the best examples of a breed are heterozygotes, then once good specimens were obtained, future selected winners would be expected to be heterozygotes, as occurs with the English. And many more breeds may contain a mixed pair of genes than is generally realised. If the homozygotes do not give the exhibition form they would be rejected at selection – consequently the purity of established breeds not need concern the hobbyist.

Progressive line-breeding to one rabbit will maintain his contribution to future generations and by full sib matings (brother to sister), it is possible that the Coefficient of In-breeding will approach 100 per cent, the condition when the ancestry of all rabbits can be traced back to just two individuals. In practice, total in-breeding can never be achieved and should not be sought as the maximum improvements will have been obtained with the early matings. Further close-breeding will result in minimal improvement with maximum build-up of harmful genes. Even for exceptionally good animals, it is doubtful whether there is any advantage in increasing their combined contribution above 60–70 per cent. Introduction of an out-cross, or a line-breeding programme, will introduce an important hybrid vigour to the line.

THE BREEDS OF RABBIT

There is no totally satisfactory method of classifying the breeds of rabbit. Alphabetical order is confusing as breeds adjacent to each other probably share no genetic relationship. Moreover, the name is usually no more than an arbitrary one. To overcome the problem, this chapter classifies the breeds, as far as possible, according to their genetic composition, a method which results in similar breeds being grouped together. However, for some breeds, i.e. those which carry more then one mutant gene, the classification must remain an arbitrary one.

The breed descriptions which follow should not be taken as breed standards or standards of perfection. These can only be obtained from the appropriate national body of the rabbit Fancy. The genetics have been deduced from an examination of several breeds and varieties and a study of the breed standards and the standards of perfection.

Where a particular gene pair may vary, the homozygous pair of the highest allele in that series has been quoted. In a few cases, due to the existence of various strains, perhaps of vastly different origins, more than one genetic make-up may be possible.

SPOTTED RABBITS

DUTCH

Origin
The Dutch came from stock imported into the UK during the last century from the Netherlands. The genetics are extremely complicated and there appear to be two recessive genes ($du^w du^w$) responsible for the main pattern. However, modifiers probably influence the major markings – the stops, cheek and saddle – independently. One of the problems associated with the breed is that heavily marked and lightly marked specimens often occur in most strains and these can be mated with successful results in a way similar to that employed with Selfs and Charlies.

Description
This cobby rabbit is short in the back with a general round appearance at the rear. The head markings consist of coloured cheeks reaching down to the smellers (whiskers). These are separated by a wedge-shaped white marking

extending from the jaw and meeting at a point just between the ears. The black marking covers the ears and extends just behind them. The saddle (back marking) commences just behind the front legs and covers the rest of the body, with the exception of the tail and the last 3 cm ($1\frac{1}{4}$ in) of the hind legs, which remain white. In the ideal specimen, there is a sharp demarcation between the colour and the white markings. The Dutch has brown eyes, in the black variety.

Colours and Genetics

UK	USA	Genotype
Black	Black	$aadudu$ or E^dE^ddudu
Blue	Gray	$aaddudu\star$
Brown Grey	Gray	$d̶udu$
Pale Grey	Gray	$dudu$
Steel Grey	Steel Gray	$E^dE(or\ E^sE)dudu$
Tortoiseshell (Sooty Fawn)	Tortoiseshell (Sooty Fawn)	$aaeedudu$
Chocolate	Chocolate	$aabbdudu$
Yellow	Yellow	$eedudu$

$\star$The theoretically possible ddE^dE^ddudu is not quoted as it is not bred in sufficient numbers to be considered an alternative.

The Yellow Dutch has the same colour genes as the Orange Rex but the latter has a white belly whereas the Dutch has a yellow belly. This difference arises as a result of selecting for different characteristics in the two breeds.

TRICOLOUR DUTCH

Origin

This rabbit was the result of combining the genes of the Dutch with those of the Japanese (Harlequin) to produce a Harlequin Dutch.

Description

It is similar in body to the Dutch, from which it is considered to be a distinct breed rather than a colour variation. It possesses the Harlequin pattern of one orange cheek with the ear above it black, and one black cheek with the ear above orange. The rabbit has Dutch spotting but the saddle consists of alternating rings of black and orange.

Colours and Genetics

UK	USA	Genotype
Black and Orange	Not listed	e^je^jdudu

ENGLISH (English Butterfly, English Spot)

Origin

This is a naturally occurring mutation, possibly first referred to in Thomas Bewick's *History of Quadrupeds* (1792) where 'piebald' rabbits are mentioned. It has been exhibited since the last quarter of the nineteenth century.

Description

The English is a medium-weight rabbit of good type displaying all the features that would be expected from an animal of that size. It is the complex markings that present the breeder with problems. It has a butterfly smut, from which it takes its alternative name, and a coloured circle around each eye with a cheek spot underneath. The ears, which must be short and held erect, are coloured.

Running from the base of each ear to the tail is an unbroken herring-bone saddle marking. Along each side of the body, starting at the base of the ears and extending to the haunches, is a series of coloured spots. In the ideal specimen, these are sharp and well defined; they should not run into the saddle markings. In addition there is one spot on each of the legs, as well as six belly, or teat, spots. The animal possesses an overall symmetry, with both sides carrying comparable markings.

Colours and Genetics

UK	USA	Genotype
Black	Black	*aaEnen*
Blue	Blue	*aaddEnen*
Grey	Gray	*Enen*
Tortoiseshell	Tortoise	*aaeeEnen*
Chocolate	Chocolate	*aabbEnen*
–	Lilac	*aabbddEnen*
–	Gold	*eeEnen*

BLANC DE HOTOT (Hotot in USA)

Origin

The rabbit is of French origin and the breed was developed by Baroness Bernhard prior to World War 1. Genetically it shows the additive effects of the English spotting and Dutch spotting genes. The weight, of 4–4.5 kg (9–10 lb), would support the idea of crosses having been made between a 'Giant Spotted Dutch' carrying the English spotting gene, and a Standard Dutch, but the inclusion of other crosses to produce the correct body type for what is essentially a meat rabbit cannot be ruled out.

Description

It has a well-rounded thickset body of medium length. The very dense soft white fur is so lustrous as to have a frosty appearance. The only marking is a black eye circle, ideally of 23 mm width, which is completely regular and unbroken. The staring appearance of the animal is further enhanced by the jet-black eyelashes. The eyes themselves are brown in colour, showing that the rabbit does not carry the Albino gene, nor the Viennese White spotting gene which yields a blue eye. The breed carries more white than any other brown-eyed breed.

Colours and Genetics

UK	USA	Genotype
Black	Black	*aaEnen (or En) dudu*

No other colours are listed but, from simple crossing with the appropriate Selfs of similar body type, they could readily be produced. They may not have the same striking effect as the black against the white ground.

DWARF HOTOT

Origin
This is a breed of very recent origin – from the middle to late 1970s. It comes from Germany, not from the Hotot district of France. The breed was achieved by crossing dwarf stock carrying the correct gene pattern rather than by attempting to dwarf the Blanc de Hotot, which is a large animal.

Description
This rabbit, which is shown in the USA but not in the UK, has a well-rounded, cobby, dwarf, compact body. The only marking on the white body is the eye circle, which is about 1–2 mm wide.

Colours and Genetics
The coat genetics are the same as for the Blanc de Hotot above.

AMERICAN CHECKERED GIANT

Origin
It is not known from where this rabbit originated, but it almost certainly has the same genetic make-up as the English. It illustrates the importance of selection; if the two breeds have a common ancestry then selecting to different standards has resulted in the diverse patterns, although the rudiments of the same markings can be seen in both. The body of the Checkered Giant is more hare-like than that of the English and the rabbit is almost twice the weight. There is no evidence to support the belief that the wild white hare was involved in the make-up of this animal, because no cross

between a rabbit and a hare (or the domestic and other species of rabbit) has ever been shown to occur.

It is tempting to speculate that the Belgian Hare was at some stage involved in the make-up of this rabbit. Its true origin may lie in continental Europe, where other breeds of the same pelt pattern are known.

Description
It has a long well-arched body with medium hindquarters and the body is carried well off the ground. More importance is attached to body type than in the English rabbit. The markings are similar to those in the English Butterfly; there are eye circles around each eye with a spot below, and spine and tail markings. There are no chain markings emanating from the base of the ears but those on the flanks have merged together to yield areas of solid unbroken colour.

Colours and Genetics

UK	USA	Genotype
–	Black	*aaEnen*
–	Blue	*aaddEnen*

RHINELANDER

Origin
As the name implies, this is a rabbit of German origin, the result of combining the genes of the English and the Japanese, and may be considered as the English equivalent of the Tricolour Dutch although, in exhibition specimens, the called-for markings are not as strict as those specified for the English.

Description
This true tricolour rabbit has colouring consisting of black and orange-yellow with white spotting. It is a thickset rabbit, somewhat heavier than the English and well-muscled with a rounded rump. It has the typical butterfly marking, eye circles, and cheek spots, coloured ears and unbroken saddle. There are between six and eight spots on the flank, but none originate from the base of the ears. In spite of the separation of the spots, their positioning again supports the view that the Checkered Giant and the Continental European Butterfly have a common ancestor. In the Rhinelander, teat and leg spots are ignored, again emphasising the difference in selection which appears to have occurred in the UK.

Colours and Genetics

UK	USA	Genotype
Orange-Yellow, Black and White	–	*e^j e^j Enen*

VIENNESE WHITE

Origin

This breed is not listed as such by the British Rabbit Council or the American Rabbit Breeders Association, but the Blue-Eyed White, of which it may be considered the forerunner, is listed under such breeds as the Beveren, the Dwarfs and Polish. It is known on the continent of Europe as the Weisses Wiener. It is a totally white rabbit with a full wild Agouti genotype except that both dominant *V* genes are replaced by the totally recessive *vv*. The Viennese White, in any body type, is an example of total spotting, giving a Blue-Eyed Self White.

In the USA, there is a breed called the Blue Vienna which is based on the body size and fur characteristics of the White and which was an old utility breed originating in Austria during the 1890s.

Description

This is a medium-sized rabbit with good width and well-developed hindquarters. Like the Rexes, it has a coat which stands virtually upright. The coat is very dark blue and lustrous. A breed with many special features, it is almost certainly of the genotype *aadd* which confers blue eyes, as in the case of the Viennese White (hypothetical).

Colour and Genetics

UK	USA	Genotype
–	Blue	*aadd*

LOPS

A Lop is an example of selection for just one characteristic, ear length. In general, ear length is related to body size. It is a widely held view that the first Lops were a sport from English rabbits and this perhaps accounts for the increasing popularity of the broken pattern amongst many Lops. Scientific investigation has shown that, however long the ear becomes, the ratio of length to width remains approximately the same.

ENGLISH LOP

Origin

This is the original sport and dates back to at least the last century. It is the connection with the butterfly pattern rather than its country of origin which gives it the name.

Description

This is a large rabbit weighing in at 4.5–5.0 kg (10–11 lb). A record ear length of 725 mm (28$\frac{1}{2}$ in) has been measured. When the rabbit is shown, the ears should be displayed facing the observer; they should be thick, like leather, free from skin blemishes and carried on a firm ear base at the top of the skull.

Colours and Genetics
The genetics are those for the normal rabbit of the same colour (see below).

FRENCH LOP

Origin
Believed to have been developed from the English Lop and Flemish Giants, it dates from the middle of the last century.

Description
This is a massive rabbit of 4.5–5.4 kg (10–12 lb). However, the ears are far smaller than the English Lop and extend for only about 4 cm (1$\frac{1}{2}$ in) below the muzzle. The animal has a strong head which results in the ears taking on the shape of a horseshoe when viewed from the front, with the crown of the arched head being the centre of the shoe. The body of the animal gives the impression of being very strong and powerful without ever appearing to be coarse. It has a deep longish fur.

Colours and Genetics

UK	USA	Genotype
–	Solid colours	As for the corresponding self:
–	Broken colours	self together with *Enen*.

DWARF LOP

Origin
Probably from selective breeding of French Lops.

Description
Weighing in at 1.6–2.0 kg (3$\frac{1}{2}$–4$\frac{1}{2}$ lb), the Dwarf Lop is essentially a dwarf version of the French Lop, with the breed characteristic of the horseshoe carriage of the ears set upon, for the size of the breed, broad well-muscled shoulders. The whole is set off with strong chest, back and legs. The breed is only recognised in the UK where it is shown in virtually all colours.

Colours and Genetics
The genetics are those for the normal rabbit of the same colour (see below).

CASHMERE LOP

Origin
Unknown: either as the result of an accident, or more probably deliberate combination of Dwarf French Lop with the Angora gene.

Description
The breed standard insists that this is not a 'woolly Dwarf Lop'. However, with a desired hair length of 4.0–5.0 cm (1½–2 in), the rabbit almost certainly has *ll* genes of the Angora, although different selection, and possibly even the size of the body may have contributed to the diminution of the Angora hair length. It is essentially a dwarf as far as body type is concerned, either as a dwarf with long hair or as a long-haired French Lop that has been dwarfed.

Colours and Genetics

UK	USA	Genotype
Solid colours	–	As for corresponding
Broken colours	–	self together with *ll*; self together with *Enen* and *ll*.

HOLLAND LOP

Origin
This is one of the two dwarfed varieties of Lops which are recognised in the USA. The American Rabbit Breeders Association gives details of the French, Dwarf and English Lops' ancestry which points to the origin of this breed being the Netherlands.

Description
The originator, Mr de Cock, is reported as saying that the variety should conform closely to the French Lop but with a 'more lovable, good-natured expression'. It is a breed in which an apple-shaped head is sought, with the greatest width between the eyes. The body gives the impression of being massive and thickset.

Colours and Genetics

UK	USA	Genotype
–	Solid colours	As for the corresponding self:
–	Broken colours	self together with *Enen*.

MEISSNER

Origin

Probably this breed is a smaller version of the English Lop, but it is not a true miniature version.

Description

It has a longish body with a curved and well-rounded rump, which is as wide as the chest. The ears are well set on a firm base and are carried full. The ears are 30–40 cm ($15\frac{1}{2}$–16 in) long. It is a silver rabbit combined with any Self colour. The distribution of the white hairs suggests a closer comparison with the English Silver than with the French Argente and supports the idea of a UK origin.

Colours and Genetics

UK	USA	Genotypes
Black	–	*aasisi*
Blue	–	*aaddsisi*
Chocolate	–	*aabbsisi*
Lilac	–	*aabbddsisi*
Yellow	–	*eesisi*

All colours may not have been bred.

MINI LOP

Origin

Not known, but probably from the continent of Europe.

Description

This is the fourth miniaturised version of the French Lop. It differs from the others in being heavier and larger, with a body weight of 2.5–2.7 kg ($5\frac{1}{2}$–6 lb). In general terms, however, this variety, which is said to be the same as the German Kleine Widder, has the same body type as all small Lops.

To date, no miniaturised English Lop has been produced, although there seems to be little reason why this could not be achieved. It would probably take several generations for the animals to breed true to type and it would almost certainly result in some degree of change in the body type as a result of the dwarfing process.

Colours and Genetics

There is no reason why any of the Lops cannot be bred in any of the colours, coat patterns or hair-fibre types that are possible for Normal rabbits (although a Rexed coat may not be possible for the miniatures) but, with the exception of the Cashmere, only Normal coats are bred. Breed standards do restrict the colours that may be exhibited in some cases and these should be consulted for a more detailed description. The genotypes of any of the colour varieties will be the same as those of Normal breeds, and these should be studied. Because of the belief that the Lops originated from an English Butterfly, the broken or spotted pattern is very popular amongst Lops. The genotype of this pattern is almost certainly *Enen*, combined with that of the Self colours. Examples are given below.

UK	USA	Genotype
Black	Black	*aaEnen*
Orange/Yellow	Orange/Yellow	*eeEnen*
Fawn	Fawn	*ddeeEnen*
Tortoiseshell	Tortoise	*aaeeEnen*

Although the markings are by no means as strict as with the Spotted rabbits, there is a well-defined pattern in which the animal exhibits the characteristic butterfly smut. The back is coloured and the belly and chest remain white. As it lacks the genetic make-up of the English and related breeds, there is no distinct herring-bone but a shoulder spot may be produced. In exhibition specimens, the standards for the colouring are as high as in other breeds and the same depth of colour is demanded.

NORMAL SELFS
A Self-coloured rabbit is one that has the same colour markings throughout the body and no banding in the individual hairs. The main variation between the breeds are body type, fur type, size and any restrictions placed on colour.

BEVEREN

Origin
A very old utility rabbit used for many years for both meat and fur. The original Beveren, which was pale blue in colour, came from Belgium and quickly attained widespread popularity. Other colours followed, most noticeably the Blue-Eyed White.

Description
It has a well-developed mandolin-shaped body, giving the overall impression of a strong rabbit with an arched back. The fur must be both soft and dense and free from woolliness. It should have a marked lustre.

Colours and Genetics

UK	USA	Genotype
Blue	Blue	*aadd*

Black	Black	*aa*
White (Blue-Eyed)	White (Blue-Eyed)	*vv*
Brown	–	*aabb*
Lilac	–	*aabbdd*

HAVANA

Origin

In the UK, the Havana is solely a rich chocolate-coloured rabbit, a natural coloured mutation resulting from the non-development of black. In the USA, Black Havanas and Blue Havanas are shown, as well as the Chocolate. The name is used to describe the body type corresponding to that found in specimens of the original colour, rather than to describe the colour itself.

Description

The Havana, weighing 2.5–3.0 kg (5½–6½ lb) is one of the smaller meat-and-fur rabbits. It is of cobby construction with well-rounded loins – although this aspect is not as developed as in the Dutch. It has a soft dense and lustrous coat.

Colours and Genetics

UK	USA	Genotype
Chocolate	Chocolate	*aabb*
–	Black	*aa*
–	Blue	*aadd*

LILAC

Origin

The historical origin of this breed is not recorded but, since the colour is the result of a dilution of the non-development of black, it is a reasonable assumption that, as soon as the chocolates and blues came together in the Fancy, the breeds were crossed, giving the variety a reasonable antiquity, although it appears only to have been shown in this century.

Description

Although the breed is fractionally heavier than the Havana, one of the breeds which was almost certainly in its make-up, it has the same rounded cobby type. The colour is a medium dove-grey. The coat, which should not fly back, must be very dense. In the UK, it should be silky whereas in the USA it should be 'neither harsh, silky nor woolly. The only colour is that from which the breed takes its name and this should be uniform throughout the whole body.

Colours and Genetics
It has the genotype *bbdd*.

ALASKA

Origin
Of unknown origin, this is a truly all-black rabbit of medium size.

Description
A rounded rabbit, the strong rounded quarters give it an almost cobby appearance. The dense silky coat has a lustre over the back and front of the animal, although the body tends to lack this shine. Not listed for the USA, it has been known for several years in continental Europe.

Colours and Genotypes
The genotype is simply *aa*.

AMERICAN

Origin
Known in the USA since 1917, this rapidly became the most popular Blue rabbit in the country. The Albino form occurred either as a sport of the Blue or as the result of deliberate crossing of white rabbits carrying the gene for non-development of colour.

Description
The mandolin-type body is moderately arched over the loins and hindquarters with a definite taper to the shoulders. The blue colour is probably the darkest of all Blue rabbits but it involves selection rather than other major colour-conferring genes.

Colours and genetics

UK	USA	Genotype
–	Blue	*aadd*
–	White	*cc*

NEW ZEALAND

Origin
In the UK there are two distinct types of New Zealand, the Red and the other colours – White, Black and Blue. The Red is the older and has very little in common with the other colours, having a body weight of about 3.6 kg (8 lb) compared with about 5.4 kg (12 lb) for the other varieties.

Description

The Red is a medium-boned and medium-bodied rabbit with only a slight tendency towards arching of the back. The coat is unique amongst fur rabbits in being very harsh and lying close to the body. There are far more guard hairs to the fur fabric than are found in the other colours. Of the Whites, Blues and Blacks, the New Zealand White is probably the best-established meat rabbit in the world. It is not the largest breed but the medium-length body is well covered in muscle and it has a firm flesh with a strong head and broad skull set on a short neck. The back shows little tendency to rise towards the well-rounded, meat-carrying haunches. The double coat, consisting of almost separate layers of fur fabric and guard hairs, should be very dense with a soft underfur and strong guard hairs. The guard hairs are less wiry than those of the Red and possibly fewer in number.

In the USA, where the breed originated, three colours are recognised, Red, White and Black, but all three are of the same body type, weight (4–5.5 kg/9–12 lb) and fur type. They approximate to British New Zealand Whites with a well-balanced meaty body and a Normal fur type. There are no American equivalents of the British Red type or Blue colour. In New Zealand itself, only the White is currently recognised.

Colours and Genetics

The genetics of the Red may be further complicated by the presence of more than one contributory mutant; *ee* would be expected to provide, with selection, a coat approaching that called for in the breed – as would *ww*, a wide-band Agouti. The possibility that both genes have contributed to the present-day Reds cannot be ruled out.

UK	USA	New Zealand	Genotype
Red	Red	–	*ee (or ww)**
White	White	White	*cc*
Black	Black	–	*aa*
Blue	–	–	*aadd*

*Possibly very complex genetics involving colour intensifiers but there is no reason to assume that the principle involved in the USA breed is different from those of the UK breed.

PALOMINO

Origin

Indisputably an American creation. The American Rabbit Breeders Association credit Mr Young of Washington as the originator.

Description

As in most utility rabbits, the Palomino has a body of moderate length, well muscled and covered evenly with firm flesh. The back has an arch which presents a round loin and quarters. The rabbit is of a light golden shade with a creamy white undercoat (in the Golden variety) or a silvery sheen over a bright orange intermediate colour with a white base for the Lynx variety. The fur is lightly and evenly ticked with lilac.

Colours and Genetics

UK	USA	Genotype
–	Golden	*ee*
–	Lynx	*bbdd*

BLANC DE BOUSCAT

Origin

The UK breed standard attributes the breed to France. The Angora, Champagne d'Argente and Flemish Giant are said to be involved in its composition.

Description

An exceptionally large rabbit, it weighs 5–7 kg (11–15½ lb). It is well muscled and elegant with a snowy white roll-back coat. It is not bred in the USA.

Colours and Genetics

Genetically it is a simple albino (*cc*).

THURINGER

Origin

This is the Normal version of the Tortoiseshell (Sooty Fawn) and is most probably the result of crossing a fully Self Black with a Yellow and conducting sib-matings of the offspring. There appears to be no recorded history of how the breed came about but it must have been manufactured as it involves two recessive gene types.

Description

This is a medium-sized rabbit with well-developed shoulders and a rounded rump. The coat is of a yellow ochre with blackish-blue guard hairs. Patches of bluish black appear on various parts of the body, most noticeably the loins, cheeks, belly, feet and around the eyes. The weight of 2.5–4.25 kg (5½–9¼ lb) suggests that different breeds were used in the body make-up and that there is still much room for refinement of the type.

Colours and Genetics

The well-developed interspersion of the blue-black fixes its colour genetics exactly as *aaee*.

FLORIDA WHITE

Origin
Developed in the USA for small fryers and for laboratory purposes, the Dutch, Polish and New Zealand White were probably involved in its composition.

Description
A cobby and compact animal, it has well-rounded hips and hindquarters tapering to meaty shoulders. It has a Normal medium-short coat with very good fly black.

Colours and Genetics
It is a pure Albino (*cc*).

SIBERIAN

Origin
This is not known but there is nothing to suggest that it originated in the area from which it takes its name. It is a pure Self.

Description
It is a medium-sized rabbit with a short neck supported on a medium-sized body. The hair must roll back to its original position when stroked in the reverse direction.

Colours and Genetics

UK	USA	Genotype
Black	–	*aa*
Blue	–	*aadd*
Brown	–	*aabb*
Lilac	–	*aabbdd*

AGOUTI SERIES

BELGIAN HARE

Origin
This is a very old breed of rabbit and, whilst its origin is not known with any degree of certainty, it can be stated definitely that there is no trace of hare in its make-up. No cross between the rabbit and the hare, which possesses different numbers of chromosomes, has ever been authenticated. The Belgian Hare did much to help publicise rabbit-showing as a hobby at

around the turn of the century and can truly claim a place amongst the great breeds of the Fancy. Sadly it is not seen as frequently as it once was.

Description

It is quite unlike any other breed of rabbit with its thin racy body, well tucked up on muscular flanks. The back has a pronounced arch with the loins and hindquarters well rounded. The head is long and fine and the chest is narrow. The rather harsh fur is a deep rich tan or chestnut shade. The brilliant black wavy ticking on the body, and the ears distinctly laced with black, confirms that this is actually an Agouti and that the mahogany body shade is the result of the presence of the wide band.

Colour and Genetics

The genotype is almost certainly *ww* with no other genes being involved but more selection for type has probably occurred in the Belgian Hare than in any other breed. This explains why the colour today is so far removed from the sandy shade usually associated with this genetic composition.

PERLFEE

Origin

Nothing is known about the origin of this rabbit. It is an Opal.

Description

This rabbit, which is known in the UK but not in the USA, is very similar to the Havana, possessing the same cobby body and general shape. Its fur, which is very dense, has three bands: a blue base colour followed by a brown shade and finally a blue shade, giving a pearly-grey effect. The intermediate or Agouti banding shade appears as a brown triangle at the nape of the neck.

Colours and Genetics

The Opal or dilute Agouti is one of the simplest of all mutations – reduction of density of pigmentation (*bb*).

FLEMISH GIANT

Origin

A very old rabbit, whose origin is not known, this was probably one of the first meat breeds produced. In the UK only one colour is recognised and this is not a Self. However, in the USA, the breed name is applied to a range of colours of a specific body type. The American Flemish Giant is slightly heavier than its British counterpart.

Description

A large-bodied rabbit with a deep flat body and broad fore- and hindquarters. It has a moderately thick coat and a very firm flesh.

Colours and Genetics

UK	USA	New Zealand	Genotype
Steel Grey	Steel Gray	Steel Grey	E^dE or E^sE
–	Light Gray	Light Grey	EE (Normal Agouti)
–	Sandy	Sandy	ww
–	Black	Black	aa
–	Blue	Blue	$aadd$
–	White	White	cc
–	Fawn	Fawn	ee

BRITISH GIANT

Origin

This utility rabbit was originally bred for its meat. To harvest the secondary product, the pelt, it was produced in several different colours.

Description

A large rabbit with good meat characteristics, it has a large roomy body covered with good muscle development.

Colours and Genetics

UK	USA	Genotype
White (Red-Eyed)	–	cc
White (Blue-Eyed)	–	vv
Dark Steel Grey	–	E^dE (or E^sE)
Blue	–	$aadd$
Brown Grey	–	EE (Normal Agouti)

DEILENAAR

Origin

The origin is unknown but, from the breed description, it would appear that only one mutant gene, that for the wide band, is involved and that the rabbit is a true Agouti. There could be Belgian Hare in its ancestry.

Description

This is a well-rounded rabbit with a dense lustrous fur similar in colour to that of the Belgian Hare. It retains the blue undercolour of the Agouti pattern, covered by chestnut with wavy ticking.

Colour and Genetics

The underside markings can be a light tan colour similar to those seen in some Belgian Hares; together with the black ear lacy, this supports *ww*.

ISABELLA

Origin
This is probably a dilute sooty fawn; the chamois colour is the result of dilution of the yellow shade of the tortoiseshell and the blue of the dilution of the black flank markings.

Description
It has a dense, silky, loosely lying fur on a stoutly built body. It is a fine-boned rabbit. The colour is light sandy down to the skin with blue shading occurring at the flanks and muzzle and in the ticking of the ears, which is consistent with the dilution effect. Carrying self rather than Agouti genes is consistent with the colour, extending right down to the skin.

Colours and Genetics
It has the *aaddee* genes.

TANS

The Tans take their name from the black-and-tan colouring, in which the second, or underside, colour is tan. In talking about Tan rabbits, however, it is the pattern of the black and tan and not the colouring itself which is referred to. In the tan pattern, the body colour is solid and free from either misplaced hairs or white hairs. The tan colour covers the triangle at the nape of the neck, the inner part of the front and hind legs, the chest, belly and the flanks of the tail.

NORMAL TANS

Origin
This natural mutation of the Agouti series is thought first to have been encountered in Derbyshire, UK.

Description
The exhibition rabbit has a well-defined series of tan markings, a selection from the natural mutation, on a short cobby body. The short coat has a silk-like texture. In this most striking of rabbits, great importance is attached to the colour. At any exhibition of rabbits, the eye will be drawn immediately to this breed.

Colours and Genetics

UK	USA	Genotype
Black	Black	$a^t a^t$
Blue	Blue	$a^t a^t dd$

116

| Chocolate | Chocolate | a^la^lbb |
| Lilac | Lilac | a^la^lbbdd |

THRIANTA

Origin
Of unknown origin, this rabbit probably contains Tans in its make-up.

Description
Very similar to the Tan rabbit, the Thrianta is brilliant orange all over.

Colours and Genetics
The genotype to produce this effect, without very extensive selection, would be *ee*.

CHINCHILLA GROUP

Included in this group are all the rabbits which do not contain the gene for the total development of colour (*C*) or the pair of recessive genes for the non-development of colour (*cc*). Between these two extremes lie four genes which are neither totally dominant nor totally recessive with respect to the gene adjacent in the series. This makes the interpretation of the coats, which are dependent upon this series of genes, the most difficult of all due to overlap of effects. Two, or possibly more, genotypes would produce the same results. The breeder should be aware of all the possibilities and try to establish for himself which genes are present in his stud and should use the information to improve his lines. The three Chinchilla genes – Dark, Medium and Light – are the result of the failure of the yellow colour to develop by the Himalayan gene. The black is incapable of development and the Normal Agouti colour and markings have been reduced to sepia on the extremities of the body, full black or other self coloured markings only being achieved when *AA* is replaced by *aa* in the Agouti series.

CHINCHILLA

Origin
The best known of all fur rabbits, the present show specimens are derived from stock which arrived in the UK from France towards the end of World War 1 and in the USA shortly afterwards.

Description
The coat of the Chinchilla has been bred to resemble real Chinchilla fur, with a slate-blue or damson base, which should be as dark as possible, followed by an intermediate white or pearl colour topped with a narrow black line. In recent years, the tendency has been for the pearling, which must be narrower than the slate, to increase in width. The whole coat has a

wavy or mackerel effect due to the predominance of guard hairs. The coat is soft but of a firm texture. The rabbit is a fine-boned animal, moderately built and of good type.

The general description and remarks relating to the Chinchilla are equally applicable to the three weights at which the breed is shown in the USA and to the two weights bred in the UK and New Zealand, although the wording of the standards and the importance attached to certain characteristics may differ.

Colour and Genetics

The actual genetics of this rabbit are best resolved by studying the colour of the eye. The blue-speckled or grey eye, which is extensively but not exclusively kept in the UK, is almost certainly $c^{chd}c^{chd}$. The USA standard calls for a brown eye, which is most probably $c^{chd}c^{chm}$. However, due to the degree of doubt which remains it is best to quote the genetics as c^{chd} – with the second allele unresolved, or as c^{chd} $c^{chd/m}$ as the most probable gene formula. Whether homozygote or heterozygote produces the best coat pattern has not been resolved as they are similar in appearance. No eye colour restriction appears in the New Zealand standard and therefore both genotypes are acceptable.

The types of Normal-coated Chinchilla are given below.

UK	USA	New Zealand
Chinchilla	Standard Chinchilla	Standard Chinchilla
–	American Chinchilla	–
Chinchilla Giganta	Giant Chinchilla	Giant Chinchilla

FOX

Origins

The Fox is the result of crossing a rabbit carrying the Dark Chinchilla gene with a Black-and-Tan.

Description

A medium-sized fur rabbit, slightly arched in the back, it has an inclination towards cobbiness. The colouring of the Black Fox consists of a jet-black topside with white-tipped guards hairs distributed on the chest, flanks and feet and the rabbits are bred to extend this ticking as far as possible. The jaws, underside, tail and belly are all white, as is the small triangle at the nape of the neck. There is a pea spot at the front of each ear. It has the dense silky coat of the true fur rabbit. In the Blue, Chocolate and Lilac, the black is replaced with the respective colour.

Colour and Genetics

Providing that one Dark Chinchilla allele is present, the second member of

118

the C series may vary. Due to incomplete dominance, there may be a difference in the quality of the rabbits, depending upon the genotype. The allowance of either brown or grey eyes in the standard is testimony to the fact that the c^{chm} gene is probably present in some examples.

The American equivalent of the Fox is the Silver Marten and not the Silver Fox, which is a large Silver. Although there are differences in the standards, they are essentially the same breed and their genotypes may be considered together.

UK (Fox)	USA (Silver Marten)	Genotype
Black	Black	$a^t a^t c^{chd}$**
Blue	Blue	$a^t a^t c^{chd} dd$
Lilac	–	$a^t a^t c^{chd} bb dd$
Chocolate	Chocolate	$a^t a^t c^{chd} bb$
–	Sable	$a^t a^t c^{chl}$*

*This is a Light Chinchilla tan rather than a Dark Chinchilla tan but it is included in this classification as this is where it appears in the appropriate standard from where it derives its name.
**Only one Chinchilla allele is quoted as the second may be either c^{chd} or c^{chm}.

THE SABLES (SIAMESE AND THE MARTEN)

Origins

There are two classes of Sables, the Siamese, which is a 'Self Light Chinchilla', and the Marten, which is a 'Tan Light Chinchilla'. In addition, both may be obtained in Light, Medium and Dark shades.

Description

All six patterns and shades are carried on the same neat cobby body of a rabbit that is medium-sized. The coat is silky and dense. The Siamese Sable is a true Self with the saddle a deeper shade of sepia. The colour decreases in intensity down the sides and chest, but still retaining the basic sepia shade, to become lightest under the belly and the tail of the animal. In the Marten Sable, the pattern is basically that of a Tan, with the upper side, corresponding to those parts which are black in the Black and Tan, being sepia, while the underside, belly under the tail and eye circles are white. The two blend together with pale sepia, and the chest, flanks and feet are generously ticked with guard hairs, resembling the pattern of the Rex.

Colour and Genetics

UK	USA	Genotype
Marten Sable	Marten Sable	
Dark	–	$a^t a^t c^{chl} c^{chl}$
Medium	–	$a^t a^t c^{chl} c^h / c$
Light	–	
Siamese Sable	Sable	$aa c^{chl} c^{chl}$
Dark	–	

Medium	–	$aac^{ch}l_ch/c$
Light	–	

This is a simple approach to the genetics for whether a Sable is classed as Light or Medium, or possibly even Dark, will depend solely upon its appearance and the breeder is advised not to attempt to determine the genotype on appearance alone but rather to perform breeding tests. The situation is further complicated because Martens and Siamese are sometimes crossed and Martens may not even be homozygous for the Tan allele (a^t).

SMOKE PEARL

Origin
Almost certainly as a deliberate cross-breeding of animals containing the corresponding genes, i.e. a blue, light chinchilla and tan or black.

Description
The Smoke Pearl is a Dilute Sable and, as such, it is possible to obtain both the Self (Siamese) and Tan (Marten) patterns. The colour is a pearl-grey beige, with shading similar to that described above. The Dilute version of the Sable is not bred extensively in the USA.

UK	USA	Genotypes
Smoke Pearl	–	
Marten	–	$a^ta^tc^{ch}l_cchl_dd$
Siamese	–	$aac^{ch}l_cchl_dd$

SEAL POINT

Origin
As for the Smoke Pearl, although selection was made among the Rexed varieties to achieve even more desirable pelts.

Description
It is a dark sepia in colour on the points, i.e. the feet, nose, ears and tail. Whilst it is possible to see certain similarities between the Himalayan pattern and the Seal Point, there may not be Himalayan genes present in the Seal Point. In the Chinchilla series there is a gradual loss of colour, first with the failure of the yellow pigment to develop and then with the lack of black resulting in a sepia shade. Simultaneously the area that is coverable begins to decrease. The Seal Point reflects this both in the shade and the diminishing

colour on the parts of the body other than the points, again probably the result of the temperature on the pigment at the extremities of the body.

The Normal Seal Point is not bred although it does exist in the Rexed form and as the Netherlands Dwarf.

SQUIRREL

Origin
Possibly as a result of a straight cross between a Chinchilla and a blue rabbit, and the selection of the young from sib-matings.

Description
Like the Seal Point, the Squirrel is not bred in the Normal form but does exist in other breeds such as the Satin, Rex and Netherlands Dwarf.

Colour and Genetics
It is a Dilute Chinchilla of genotype $c^{chd}c^{chd}dd$.

HIMALAYAN

Origin
This is an extremely old breed involving the Himalayan gene combined with the Self to produce the colour. Of more interest is the body shape, which is unique to this breed and, in any other, would be considered a serious fault.

Description
It has a trim snaky body (see plate 16) which gives it the appearance of a tube with protruding feet and ears. The ears, feet and nose are marked whilst the rest of the body is covered in a short, fine, white fur which lies close to the body. The eyes are a ruby colour. Himalayans are born with a silver-like sheen to the coat and the markings only develop after the second moult. Their exhibition life tends to be short, as the second full adult coat seldom retains the quality of colour of the first.

Colours and Genetics

UK	USA	Genotype
Black	Black	aac^hc^h
Blue	Blue	aac^hc^hdd
Chocolate	–	$aabbc^hc^h$
Lilac	–	$aabbc^hc^hdd$

CALIFORNIAN

Origin
This famous rabbit was first exhibited, in the State from which it takes its name, in 1932, and the American Rabbit Breeders Association recorded that

121

it contains in its make-up Chinchilla, New Zealand White (which gives the body shape) and Himalayan (which is responsible for the coat markings).

Description

It is plump and full over and around the hips with a firm meaty saddle. The whole rabbit is designed to carry as much meat as possible.

Colours and Genetics

UK	USA	Genotype
Black	Black	$aac^{h}c^{h}$
Chocolate	–	$aabbc^{h}c^{h}$
Blue	–	$aac^{h}c^{h}dd$
Lilac	–	$aabbc^{h}c^{h}dd$

In New Zealand, there is a standard for the breed, but no colour is listed.

HARLEQUINS AND MAGPIES

Origin

These are the court jesters of the rabbit world and are of the penultimate gene in the non-extension-of-black series. The gene was originally called the Japanese modification, in spite of the fact that there was no evidence to suggest that the rabbit originated in that particular country. Some authorities credit France with that honour. The name probably owes its origin to the belief that exotic and different objects came from the East, and there can be few things more unusual than the Japanese rabbit.

Description

The *Harlequin* is a medium-sized rabbit, the body muscular and slightly arched. The coat is very dense and silky. The markings are as follows. The head is divided equally into one black side and one orange side. The ear on the orange side is black whilst the other is orange. Of the front legs, one is orange and the other is black while the colours of the back legs are the opposite way round. The body consists of a series of alternating black and orange bands. In the Harlequins, one colour is always golden orange.

The *Magpies* are a result of crossing the Dark Chinchilla allele with the Japanese gene. To understand this, it is necessary to think not of the rabbit which normally results from the presence of two Dark Chinchilla genes but of the genes' role in colour formation and what its effect is on the Japanese gene. This is the total non-development of yellow, which results in the elimination of colour from the yellow areas produced by the Japanese pattern, leaving white as the second colour in the Magpies, as opposed to the orange or its dilution fawn in the harlequin.

Colours and Genetics

	UK	USA	Genotype
Black Harlequin	Black and Orange	Black and Orange	$e^j e^j$
Blue Harlequin	Blue and Fawn	Blue and Fawn	$dde^j e^j$
Brown Harlequin	Brown and Orange	Chocolate and Orange	$bbe^j e^j$
Lilac Harlequin	Dove Grey and Fawn	Dove Gray and Fawn	$bbdde^j e^j$
Black Magpie	Black and White	Black and White	$c^{chd}c^{chd}e^j e^j$ ★
Blue Magpie	Blue and White	Blue and White	$c^{chd}c^{chd}dde^j e^j$
Brown Magpie	Brown and White	Chocolate and White	$bbc^{chd}c^{chd}e^j e^j$
Lilac Magpie	Dove Grey and White	Dove Gray and White	$bbc^{chd}c^{chd}dd$

*As with all genotypes involving the Chinchilla series, other genes may be involved and the rabbits may not be homozygous for c^{chd}. The possibility of ee^j replacing the homozygous $e^j e^j$ may also be considered when planning breed improvements.

SILVERS

Origin

There are two types of silver rabbits: those of British origin, termed Silvers, and the French Argentes. Both owe their existence to the white hairs which occur from time to time in all breeds. Careful selection of these sports occurred many years ago. Silver rabbits are of great antiquity, as their pelts have been particularly sought after for cloaks and ceremonial dress. The silver patterns established are hereditary in nature and have been incorporated into a range of colours.

Description

The Silver rabbit is of light to medium size and type, with the emphasis placed on the colour and evenness of the silvering.

Colours and Genotypes

Description	UK	USA	Genotype*
Black with white hairs	Grey Silver	Gray Silver	aasisi
Orange with silver hairs	Fawn Silver	Fawn Silver	eesisi
Chestnut with white hairs	Silver Brown	Brown Silver	wwsisi

*The convention of referring to silvering as recessive si is adhered to but it is unlikely that this is a true allele but rather the result of hereditary selection.

ARGENTES

Origin

The original breed, the Argente de Champagne, is thought to have come from the Champagne district of France.

Description

The Argentes contain more white hairs than the Silvers and, in the Argente de Champagne, it is black guard hairs which give the rabbit the old-silver effect. The Argente Bleu is genetically a Dilute Champagne and both have similar pelts, hair and body types. The standards of the four colours – Champagne, Bleu, Brun and Creme – are not identical nor are they identical to those of the English Silvers. The Argente Brun and the Argente Creme are silver versions of chocolate and yellow respectively.

Colours and Genotypes

	UK	USA	Genotype
Black with white hairs	Argente de Champagne	–	*aasisi*
Blue-grey with white hairs	Argente Bleu	–	*aaddsisi*
Chocolate with white hairs	Argente Brun	–	*aabbsisi*
Yellow/Orange with white hairs	Argente Creme	–	*eesisi*

REXES AND SATINS

Origins

Both the Rexes and the Satins are simple single mutations of the Normal hair type. A definite body type has been bred over the years and the fur has become very refined. Both are bred in a range of colours and, since they all possess the same fur and body type, the colour of the pelt will be the result of the same genetic composition as for the Normal fur rabbit. They are all considered together. The list below gives the colours bred in the UK, USA and New Zealand, although it is reasonable to suppose that this will alter from time to time. Since, in any one country, the bodies of each breed are identical all genetically possible breeding combinations may be attempted.

Descriptions

The *Rex* rabbit is well proportioned with well-rounded hips and quarters exemplifying its dual role of fur and meat rabbit. The fur is very short and the guard hairs are no longer conspicuous. The fur is silky, extremely dense and free from both harshness and woolliness.

The *Satins* are similar in size to the Rexes, the body being arched and inclined to cobbiness. The most striking feature of the breed is the coat, which has a most exquisite silk-like texture and a brilliant sheen.

Colours and Genetics

UK	USA	New Zealand	Genotype
Selfs			
Ermine	White R and S	White/Ermine	$ccrr/sasa$
Black	Black R and S	Black	$aarr/sasa$
Blue	Blue R and S	Blue	$aaddrr/sasa$
Havana	–	Havana	$aabbrr/sasa$
Nutria	Chocolate R and S	Nutria	$aabbrr/sasa$
Red	Red R and S	Red	$eerr/sasa$
Orange	–	Orange	$eerr/sasa$
Lilac	Lilac R	Lilac	$aabbddrr/sasa$
Fawn	–	–	$ddeerr/sasa$
Agouti			
Castor	Castor R	Castor	rr[1]
Cinnamon	–	Cinnamon	$bbrr/sasa$
Opal	Opal	Opal	$ddrr/sasa$
Lynx	Lynx R	Lynx	$ddbbrr/sasa$
Chinchilla	Chinchilla R and S	Chinchilla R and S	$c^{chd}c^{chd}rr/sasa$
Sables			
Sable	Siamese Sable	Siamese Sable	$aac^{chl}c^{chl}/c^h/crr/sasa$[4]
–		Marten Sable (Seal Marten)	$a^ta^tc^{chl}c^{chl}/c^h/crr/sasa$[4]
Smoke Pearl	–	Smoke Pearl	$a^ta^tac^{chl}c^{chl}/c^h/cddrr/sasa$
Foxes	–		
Black	–	Black	$a^ta^tc^{chd}c^{chd}rr/sasa$
Blue	–	Blue	$a^ta^tc^{chd}c^{chd}ddrr/sasa$
Chocolate	–	Chocolate	$a^ta^tc^{chd}c^{chd}bbrr/sasa$
Lilac	–	Lilac	$a^ta^tc^{chd}c^{chd}bbddrr/sasa$
Tans	–	–	
Black	–	–	$a^ta^trr/sasa$
Blue	–	–	$a^ta^tddrr/sasa$
Chocolate	–	–	$a^ta^tbbrr/sasa$
Lilac	–	–	$a^ta^tbbddrr/sasa$
Otters	–	–	[2]
Dalmatian	Broken	Bicolour	

		Dalmatian	$aaEnenrr$[3]
Tricolour	–	Tricolour	$Enene^Je^Jrr$
Harlequin[5]	–	Harlequin	e^Je^Jrr
Himalayan	Californian	Himalayan (Californian)	$aac^hc^hrr/sasa$
Silver Seal	–	–	$aasisirr$[1]

1 Probably not bred as a Satin.
2 As for Foxes, but with no selection for silvering on the sides, this being replaced with selection for yellow colour intensities. Tan and chinchilla alleles involved.
3 *aa* may be replaced by genes for any colour; Satins almost certainly not bred in this pattern.
4 See notes on normal Sables and Smoke Pearls to see various genetic possibilities.
5 Other colour genetics may replace the Blacks and the whole range of Rexed Harlequins and Magpies is possible.

All the colours which are listed as acceptable have not necessarily been bred.

OTHER TYPES OF REX

Three other types of Rex rabbits are recognised in the UK.

The *Satin Rex* is a breed in which the Rex and Satin characteristics have been combined to give a dense soft satin-like texture free from protruding guard hairs. It may be produced in any of the colours or patterns available to Normal Rexes simply by crossing the appropriate Normal Rex with a Normal Satin. The genetics are *--rrsasa*, where -- represents the two or more genes necessary for the colour and coat pattern.

The *Astrex* or *Rough-Coated Rex* includes a new mutation for curling which is combined with the Normal Rex – both varieties share a common body type. The genetics are *--rrwawa*, where -- represents the two or more genes necessary for the colour and pattern, which may be the same as for any Normal.

The Opossum Rex is an Angora Rex whose make-up includes silvering. The overall effect is a dense soft fur, covered with white curly guard hairs. The type is similar to that of other Rexes. It can be produced in any colour. The genetics are *--llrrsisi*, where -- represents the genes necessary to produce Self colour. It is exhibited in the UK and New Zealand.

ANGORAS

There are two breeds of Angoras, the English, which has been selected to provide a far larger number of fur fibres than guard hairs, and as a consequence has a soft silky texture, and the French Angora, which has been bred to provide a larger number of primary guard hairs than its English equivalent, although it is unlikely that they exceed the fur fibres.

ENGLISH ANGORA

Origins
Both the English and the French Angoras could have originated either from

the same source or independently but there is no reason to suppose that they contain a different hair-lengthening gene. Popular belief is that the mutation first arose in Turkey where Angora sheep and goats have been reared since earliest times. Mentions of the breed were made in both France and Germany during the latter half of the eighteenth century.

Description
It has a round cobby body with a uniform length of wool which gives an overall ball shape. The ears are covered with furnishings of long hair. The legs, feet and tail are covered with fur to the ends. The fur itself should be as dense as possible with a silky texture, the ideal length being about 6.5–9.5 cm ($2\frac{1}{2}$–$3\frac{1}{2}$ in). It is exhibited in the UK, USA and New Zealand.

Colour and Genetics
Both the English and the French Angoras are coat mutations and, as in the case of the Rexes and Satins, they can be bred in all colours and patterns. However, the English Angora is essentially a utility rabbit and, before a colour is produced, its use for wool should be considered in conjunction with any breed standards. Angoras are mainly bred in Selfs, Agouti (including mutated Agoutis) and shaded Selfs (Sables, Smoke Pearls and Seals). The genetics of any coloured Angora is that for the colour-conferring gene together with *ll* for the lengthening of the wool.

FRENCH ANGORA
Origin
See under the English Angora above.

Description
The French Angora is longer and narrower in type than the English and is not so ball-shaped in appearance. The long hair does not extend to the extremities, and the feet, legs and ears appear relatively free from wool compared with the rest of the body. The hair is coarser than that of the English but of similar length. The French Angora is not bred in the UK but is established in the USA and New Zealand.

Colours and Genetics
See under the English Angora above.

SWISS FOX

Origin
This rabbit is of continental European origin and shows a further type of Angora fur.

Description

It differs from the Angoras in having a fur length of 4–7 cm ($1\frac{1}{2}$–2 in) and from the English Angora in not having furnishing on the ears. It has a small well-rounded body with well-developed muscles.

Colours and Genetics

The genetics of the colours which are recognised in the UK are probably White (*ccll*), Black (*aall*) and Havana (*aabbll*) – the same as in the English and French equivalents. The breed is, as yet, not listed for either the USA or New Zealand.

POLISH (IN UK OR BRITTANIA PETITE IN USA)

Origin

This breed probably originated by gradual selection over the years to produce the required type of rabbit. Multi-gene systems would be required to result in a viable small rabbit but, once established, other colours could be bred by suitable out-crosses followed by selection. Once all the major genes had been established, it was possible to recreate the two or more mutation varieties from completely Polish stock rather than by breeding from the Normal varieties.

Description

It is a neat compact sprightly rabbit which is judged on its toes, in a similar position to a sitting dog. It has a neat compact body with fine bones. The ears touch each other from the base to the top. The fur is fine, short and close.

Colours and Genetics

In the UK, virtually all the Selfs, Shaded Selfs, Agouti and Tan patterns, together with Tortoiseshell, Steel and Himalayan, are listed with provision for Any Other Variety. It does not necessarily follow that all forms have been created but a sufficient number has been achieved to enable the fancier to breed for him or herself any variety he could wish. Both Red-Eyed and Blue-Eyed Whites are well known.

In the USA, only the Blue-Eyed White is recognised – as the Brittania Petite.

Colours and Genetics

The pelt genetics are identical to those of the corresponding Normal varieties and these should be consulted to establish the genotypes. It is possible, in those breeds where more than one genotype can occur, such as the Chinchilla, that the genetics adopted for the Normal breed may not be identical with those of the miniature versions. However, the same arguments apply, irrespective of body size.

POLISH (USA)

Origin

It is impossible to state the exact origin of the breed but it is probably a descendant of the Dutch as it has a cobby body not unlike that of the marked rabbit. At 1.58 kg (3½ lb) it is smaller than the Dutch but larger than the English Polish which weighs a maximum of 1.13 kg (2½ lb).

Description

The body is small and compact with well-rounded hips. The fur is short, fine and dense. The head is medium full and short with a slight curvature from nose to ear.

Colours and Genetics

UK	USA	Genotype
–	Black	*aa*
–	Blue	*aadd*
–	Chocolate	*aabb*
–	Blue-Eyed White	*vv*
–	Red-Eyed White	*cc*

NETHERLANDS DWARF

Origin

This breed may well have originated in the country from which it took its name. It first came to the UK after World War 2 and was accepted by the American Rabbit Breeders Association in 1969.

Description

At 0.9 kg (2 lb) this is the smallest of all rabbits. It has a short compact body with a round head, a broad skull and bold eyes. The coat is short, dense and roll-back.

Colours and Genetics

The widest range of colours is recognised in both the UK and the USA. As with the Polish, the pelt genetics may be obtained by comparison with those of the corresponding Normal breed.

As with all miniature rabbits, the Netherlands Dwarf is only bred in the Normal fur varieties. There could be some problems associated with the body's heat retention if a Rexed coat were to be incorporated into such breeds, although an Angora version should be viable.

SHOWING RABBITS

Control of the exhibition of rabbits is exercised by national bodies, to which are affiliated national specialist breed clubs and local breed or all-breed clubs. The national breed clubs and associations either license judges or have a system of recognition of judges, and they lay down strict rules to govern the Fancy. They award championships to any rabbit that satisfies their defined criteria for that particular honour. Whilst there are many similarities in the way that the national bodies function, there are also differences. The would-be exhibitor must join his national body (membership of which is compulsory) as the first step (the addresses of the national bodies are listed in Appendix II). The national body will furnish the rules and regulations governing the Fancy in that country, as well as providing full details of specialist clubs which award many special prizes to its members and membership of which, if not compulsory, is strongly recommended; they will also furnish the addresses of local clubs and information relating to all rabbit matters. Through the various systems, advisors exist who will be only too pleased to help any newcomers, either in matters of rabbit husbandry or by introducing them to the Fancy scene. No novice should feel left out; once he or she has registered as a breeder, all that needs to be done is to ask any questions that he or she may have.

EXHIBITING

In the UK, there are several types of show, but they may be split into two categories: those which count towards a championship and those which do not. Championship shows themselves are of different status; this is denoted by the star rating, the one-star show being the lowest and the five-star being the highest. A rabbit wins a championship by collecting the appropriate number of stars; consequently there is more kudos in winning at a five-star show than at a one-star show. Championship shows may be run for all breeds. These are often but not always run in conjunction with an agricultural show, where they attract many visitors and prove an important shop window for the Fancy. Alternatively the championship show may be run by either a national or regional breed club, independently or in conjunction with another show, and be restricted to only one breed. The championship shows may be for young stock, the current year's breeding stock under a certain age, adult stock or any age. It is common in any age shows to have classes for young immature rabbits, which must be under a certain age, the actual age being stated in the standard of the breed. At non-championship shows the rabbits are often kept in their boxes and brought out for examination (table shows). Such shows allow you to assess the value of an untried youngster or other rabbit against lesser opposition than that found in a more senior show.

In the USA, overall control of the Fancy is vested in the American Rabbit Breeders Association. This issues sanction to chartered organisations to hold official shows, licenses judges and awards Grand Championships. Again shows may be divided into speciality clubs which cater for only one breed (and these may be either national, state or local) and all-breed shows having similar geographical divisions.

The ARBA has instigated a pedigree system which is central to the registration of the rabbits. In the left ear the private number is tattooed, whilst in the right ear the registration seal is placed by one of the licensed registrars appointed in every state and in Canada. To register a rabbit, the owner must be a member of ARBA and have a three-generation pedigree for the animal. The registration tattoo contains a number and this forms the basis of the registration certificate.

There are three classes of registration:
a) the Association's seal alone, which denotes that, although the rabbit is registered, its parents are not;
b) red and white seals which are awarded where first and second generations are registered;
c) red, white and blue seals which are awarded where all three generations are registered.

As with the UK system, change of ownership is registered on payment of a fee.

The Rabbit Council of New Zealand performs a similar role in overseeing the Fancy in its country and the ringing system adopted uses the same size rings as those employed in the UK, for the registration of animals.

Rabbit shows are advertised in the UK in the magazine *Fur and Feather* and, in the USA, in *Domestic Rabbits*.

JUDGING

Anyone who wishes to show any form of livestock must be aware of the criteria on which judges base their decisions so that they may first assess the quality of their own animals before putting them in competition with the efforts of other breeders. In that sense all exhibitors are judges. Indeed, judging the quality of your own livestock is the most difficult of all the arts which you will have to master if you are to become a successful exhibitor. The earlier you learn to evaluate the potential of any individual animal the sooner you can remove the failures from the rabbitry, thus allowing for more litters to be bred and increasing the chances of winning. Should you aspire to becoming a judge you will require an exhaustive knowledge not only of your own breed but also of all other breeds and varieties, as, for your initial appointments, you will probably be asked to judge at small all-breed shows. You will need to be able to evaluate specimens from one breed against those of another breed in order to place them in the correct order in the Duplicate classes.

The appropriate national body will advise any aspiring judge of the formal qualifications which are required but, in addition to expert knowledge, you will require tact and diplomacy and no one should accept an appointment unless he or she is prepared to act with humility. A judge should always remember that it is a great honour to be asked to adjudicate other people's efforts and that shows are run for the benefit of exhibitors and not of judges.

Many judges keep a mental picture of the perfect specimen in their mind's eye and tend to evaluate the actual rabbits that they are judging against this ideal. In this way it is possible to compare a Rex with a fur rabbit and a fancy breed, such as a Belgian Hare, to arrive at the Best in Show. However accurate your knowledge of the perfect specimens may be, and it needs to be very accurate indeed, it is only possible to judge the specimens that are put on the table, and, as with all forms of judging, it is a question of judging the animals shown on the day. This is important; you cannot decide how good an animal will be when the moult has finished, although a little latitude is allowable with young stock who are in a state of almost persistent moult. Any judge, prior to examining individual specimens, will examine the whole class in order to ascertain the overall standard of the animals that have been put in front of him.

GENERAL FACTORS IN THE ASSESSMENT OF RABBITS

TYPE
This term refers to the overall shape of the rabbit and, whilst there are many similarities between the various types, there are also some very large differences.

General Type
This is often referred to simply as good type (Figs. 17 and 18) and is the type meant when there is no definite mention of shape in the standard. A rabbit of good type can be described as four-square, 'like a brick', with the shoulders as wide as the pelvis, no narrowing of either the front or the back of the body and no pinching of the loins. The back should be reasonably flat, although some upward slope towards the rear end is allowable.

Cobby
This is a rabbit which is far shorter in the back, with the hindquarters well rounded, giving an all-over rounder effect than that of the general type. It is essentially a short-coupled animal and should display no signs of excessive fat.

(a)

(b)

Fig. 17. A rabbit of poor type. From the side (a), this rabbit shows signs of undernourishment at all stages of its development. It is weak-boned, the hind leg being thrown out in a very poor stance and suggesting that the animal is cow-hocked. It is very fine-boned and there is no muscle on the body. It is of very poor type all round. From above (b), note the narrowing of the shoulders and the very weak head with the eyes clearly visible from the top. In a meat breed of this type, the head is almost certainly weak.

Mandolin Type

The main difference between this and the general type is that the back slopes gently, rising towards the hindquarters, so that if the animal is viewed from the side it gives the overall silhouette of a mandolin.

SHAPE

In addition to these main types there are shapes that are applicable to just one breed.

Fully Arched

This is the term used to describe the athletic appearance of the Belgian Hare in which the backbone has a far greater curvature than that seen in any other breed. Not only must it be well muscled but it must give the appearance of being capable of running – the greyhound of the rabbit kingdom.

(a)

(b)

Fig. 18. A rabbit of good type. The side view (a) shows a well-nourished animal with good muscle cover but not fat. The back line is smooth and well rounded with no tendency to be 'chopped off' at the rear. The stance is good and the body strong and firm without being coarse. From above (b), the body is good and strong with the shoulders virtually as wide as the hindquarters. The midriff shows no tendency to be pinched in.

Snaky

In virtually all breeds other than the normal Himalayan, where it is the sought-after type, snakiness is looked upon as a very serious fault. A snaky rabbit is one that has a long thin body held close to the ground. It must not be confused with a thin rabbit for, although it gives the appearance of not having been fed properly, this is certainly not the case. An overfed Himalayan simply has a fat snaky appearance. Nor is it the result of poor bone development, but rather selective breeding to achieve the long thin appearance.

Ball

When an Angora is well combed and correctly presented, it has a well-rounded ball shape and it is this overall effect that the exhibitor is trying to create with this particular breed.

Dwarf

The dwarf type is rather squat in all respects, with a large head that is out of proportion to the rest of the body. The type demands that the animal is firm-boned, and that the dwarfing shows no signs of being due to malnutrition. The front legs must be straight, again a sign of good feeding from birth, otherwise rickets will cause the legs to curve out in a 'Queen Anne' effect. A good, round, bold head should be well set upon the body. Compared with other breeds, the pert ears are smaller in relation to the rest of the body.

Polish
The Polish is unique in that it is shown, rather like a dog, in a sitting position. It should have good straight legs and a straight back from rump to shoulders, set on firm quarters. It should possess a bold eye with ears that touch each other from their roots to the tips.

BONE STRUCTURE

In most breeds poor bone structure is described as spindly or, where there is insufficient thickness for the body type, as too fine. This may be due either to genetic factors or to insufficient calcium or vitamin D in the feed at some stage in the animal's life, particularly whilst it is still young and before the bones have properly calcified. The young embryos will be particularly vulnerable whilst they are still in the uterus. Calcium replacement occurs throughout the animal's life and it is important to maintain an adequate supply at all stages. With pelleted food no problem is likely to occur, unless insufficent rations are provided. In this case the daily rations should obviously be increased. Thick bones, out of proportion to the rest of the body are almost certainly hereditary rather than the result of overfeeding or of a diet that is too high in calcium. Overfeeding will manifest itself as obesity but does not cause thickening of the bones.

Good-boned specimens are described as fineboned where a light bone is being sought (in breeds such as the Belgian Hare) or strong-boned where a firmer structure is required (as in the New Zealand White or Californian breeds).

HEAD
The head (Fig 19) is the most obvious secondary sex feature and the sex of a rabbit should be apparent just by examining the head which is far broader in the buck than in the doe. A good head will be in perfect balance with the rest of the body, generally broad and large enough for the body type and with strong jaws. There should be a good bite with the top jaw meeting the bottom jaw exactly. The mouth should be neither overshot (where the top jaw protrudes beyond the bottom jaw) nor undershot (where the bottom jaw protrudes beyond the top jaw).

The ear base should be sufficently broad to carry and support the ears. The head should not be pear-shaped, i.e. large at the top with a good ear base but long and narrow at the muzzle with a weak jaw. Nor should it be snipey,

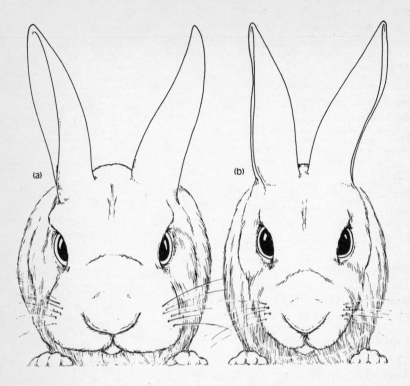

Fig. 19. The head of the rabbit. A good head (a) is strong and bold with no tendency to narrowing towards the jaws. There is a good firm ear base with well-set ears. A bad head (b) is far weaker-boned throughout. The eyes tend to be very prominent in a breed where this is not a virtue, and there is a narrowing towards the jaws. There is poor support for the ears.

i.e. thin and poorly developed and altogether too narrow for the rest of the body. A head which is too heavy and too wide for the body is described as coarse, and this also must be avoided. Dwarf breeds require a well-rounded head and this is a prominent part of the animal's make-up.

Buck teeth (in which the front two incisors protrude beyond the bite level and can be seen when the rabbit has its mouth closed) are a major hereditary fault for which animals are usually disqualified. Any animal displaying this characteristic should be omitted from the breeding programme, whatever other virtues it may possess.

EARS

Good ear carriage infers that the ears are growing upright from a firm base. Where the ears bend over or flop this is a fault (except in Lops) and is sufficient to ensure that the animals will not receive a place in any worthwhile competition. This flopping of the ears can arise during the intermediate or later stages of the rabbit's development. It is sometimes possible to remedy the problem by binding the ears together with medical tape and leaving them for about a fortnight. The tape should be removed carefully, any remaining gum being dissolved away with methylated spirits.

FEET

Rabbits do not have pads to their feet, which should be neat with toe nails of the colour specified in the standard, otherwise the animal will be disqualified. Toe nails must be trimmed for shows to avoid loss of points for condition. Barred feet, i.e. feet of a different colour from the rest of the pelt, usually a lighter shade, are a serious fault in most fur breeds.

LEGS

Both front and back legs must be straight. The front legs should show no sign of bowing and the back legs should not be cow-hocked i.e. with the knees bent inwards to meet each other. The hind legs in meat rabbits should be well covered in flesh.

BACK

The back should have evenness of form, with full shoulders and hips. There should be no sign of pinching and the whole structure should be covered with muscle, a sign of good condition.

TAIL

The carriage of the tail should be upright, lying against the base of the spine from which it orginates. It should not be carried from side to side, nor should it screw out away from the body of the rabbit.

COLOUR

Breed standards state the colour. It is not always possible to describe the colours accurately in words, so try to familiarise yourself with the shade of regular winners, as this is the generally accepted interpretation of the colour required. In Selfs colour should go down to the base of the hair. As the shaft comes to the conclusion of its growth phase the rate of deposition of pigment decreases. Colour down to the skin is the result of good hair development and as such is a much sought-after characteristic. Some people believe that in assessing the colour of a rabbit you should start at the base of the hair and work up to the tip. Whilst a sparkling top colour is absolutely essential for any show specimen, in sorting out the winners the base colour is of the utmost importance, and perhaps more than any other factor reflects the skill of the breeder. With the Agouti class of rabbit, (i.e. all rabbits that have the three-banded markings whether they are pure Agoutis or specimens carrying bb, c^{chd}, c^{chd}, dd mutant genes) there must be a clean demarcation termed the *definition*, between the individual bands. You must be able to

137

recognise whether a narrow-band gene or a wide-band gene is present for the intermediate colour, yet still appreciate the effects of widening or narrowing the band as a result of selective breeding.

EYES

The colour of these is also defined in the breed standard and, in general, should complement the main body colour. Both eyes must be of the same colour, even for those breeds that allow a choice of either blue or brown eyes. Wall eyes, those in which part of a brown iris is coloured blue, will result in disqualification. They are mainly encountered in the Dutch and are usually found in specimens that have a far greater area covered with white spotting, although it can be found in near-perfect specimens. There is a school of thought that advocates breeding Dutch rabbits from a cross between very white specimens and very dark specimens, in a similar manner to which English are bred. Even using ths scheme all examples of wall eyes must be culled, as, once established in a stud, they can prove almost impossible to remove. Eyes should be a prominent feature of the head and should be of sufficient size, any animal with small piggy eyes should be passed over. It is particularly important that the eyes are bold in the Dwarf breeds, whilst in the Albino they should have a deep ruby colour.

FUR

Fur is one of the most important characteristics of many breeds and it is assessed according to colour, texture, overall density and length.

The Normal Coat

The general feel of the coat is referred to as the *texture* and may be best assessed by brushing the coat with the hand from the tail towards the head against the grain. You should notice such things as the resistance to flow, which is a function of the thickness of the hair shaft and the softness or coarseness of the coat. It is difficult to distinguish exactly what is responsible for certain 'feel' sensations, but a high ratio of fur fibre to guard hairs, and of secondary to primary guard hairs, as well as possibly thinner hair shafts, will all contribute to an increase in softness or silkiness. The reverse will result in a far coarser feel to the coat. The fancier should familiarise himself with coarse coats, such as that of the English New Zealand Red the texture of which is due to a predominance of guard hairs. The density depends upon the number of hairs (both fur fibre and guard hairs) per square centimetre. To ascertain the density, blow into the fur; the smaller the area of skin which can be seen, the denser the coat. In a really dense coat it should be almost impossible to see the skin. Density will vary throughout the coat, so it is necessary to blow the pelt in several different positions. Two types of coat are frequently called for: the roll-back coat, in which the fur rolls back slowly to its original position when stroked in the reverse direction to which the hair grows, and the fly-back coat which rapidly returns to its original

Blowing into the pelt will reveal how dense the coat is. In a very dense coat such as this one, it will be almost impossible to see the skin. The procedure should be repeated at several points on the pelt as the density will vary.

position. The length of coat is important even in those breeds where exact dimensions are not called for – a longer coat is preferable to a short one but texture and density should be considered more important than sheer length when assessing the coat of any fur breed. Whilst all the factors discussed are important contributions to the make-up of the pelt, it is the overall character that must be used to distinguish between the specimens on the show table and to decide the relative importance attached to the fur when assessing one breed against another.

Rex

The fur of the Rex rabbit should have a velvet-like appearance. This is the result of the dense hairs growing upright. Rex coats should have about the same density as normal fur but the hairs should not protrude above the level of the fur fibre.

Angora

The Angora fur should be very dense and be silky soft to the touch, the length of fur being 6–9cm ($2\frac{1}{2}$–$3\frac{1}{2}$in). With Angora wool, the problem of mats can occur; should they be seen the rabbit will be penalised, as they are a fault of condition.

The French Angora, not shown in the UK has a far coarser coat, the result of the guard hairs predominating at the expense of the fur fibre, the reverse of that found in the English Angora.

139

POSING FOR SHOW

Different breeds, because of their various types and conformation, are shown in different positions. Whilst the judge will set them in the correct position in order to appreciate fully the quality of the animal, regular handling on the rabbitry table will soon train most animals to show themselves off to the best advantage. There are exceptions, such as the Polish, which must be sat up, and particularly the English Lop, which must be shown with its large ears displayed in front of the head with the insides facing forward.

CONDITIONING FOR SHOW

To win with any animal it is necessary for it to be in prefect condition. There are methods of feeding and grooming that are sometimes recommended to bring the rabbits up to tiptop condition. These should never be considered as alternatives to good year-round rabbit-keeping. All stock should be maintained in prime condition through good feeding and keeping the hutches clean. Regular grooming will ensure that the moult is completed in the shortest possible time as the hair follicles will be stimulated, as a result of the activity, to begin regenerating the new shaft. A good even diet will ensure that top-quality hair forms and that pigmentation develops down to the base of the hair shaft. It is just as important to ensure that the animal is not too fat as it is to ensure that there is sufficient meat on it. When the judge places his hands upon the animal he will be seeking to establish whether the bones are well covered with firm muscle tissue rather than flabby fat. If, as a result of your routine examination of the animal, you detect the development of fat, gradually reduce the quantity of food provided. Sudden drops in food quantity, as well as being cruel, will result in the animal having a loose-fitting skin, until it has had the opportunity to adjust to the new body size.

Regular grooming is best performed with a comb and a very soft brush or a gloved hand. Tweezers must not be used to remove any excess hair, such as white hairs appearing in a coloured coat or long guard hairs in the Rex breeds, or to adjust the lines in Fancy breeds such as Dutch and English. This is cheating and those caught are punished according to the rules of the Fancy.

Appendix I: AILMENTS AND DISEASES
BY DR T. REED

REPRODUCED FROM: *A PROGRESSIVE PROGRAM FOR RAISING BETTER RABBITS AND CAVIES*

BACTERIAL DISEASES

DISEASE/CONDITION	SIGNS	CAUSE	TREATMENT	PREVENTION
MASTITIS (Blue Breast)	Inflamed, swollen, hot, discoloured mammary system – all or individual sections. Abcessation of gland is common. Normally occurs just after kindling or after weaning.	Any bacteria within the mammary system. Usually a *Staphylococcus* sp. or *Streptococcus* sp.	Treat for 3 days in succession with penicillin G injection intramuscularly at 200,000 IU/10 lb body weight. Strip glands free of milk. Hot-Pak application 3-4 times daily.	Prevention of caked breast and trauma to the breast (see caked breast).
WEEPY EYE	Matted fur at medial corner and under lower lid of eye. Discharge from eye.	Inflammation of conjunctiva – most common in 'Bulldog' head type. Usually a result of blocked duct between lower eyelid and the nasal area. Usually a history of respiratory infections.	Instill neomycin ophthalmic 2-3 times per day for 3-4 days. Opening of nasolacrimal duct by professional help.	Prevent respiratory diseases.
VENT DISEASE (Rabbit syphilis)	'Scabby' inflammation of genitals – both sexes – can have scabs on nose and mouth in later stages; 'scabby nose', refuses to mate and/or conceive. Abortions.	Spirochete organism *Treponema cuniculi*. Usually spread through mating.	Daily application of penicillin G ointment to the external genitals or daily administration of penicillin G intramuscularly for 3 days, 200,000 IU/10 lb body weight.	Always check breeding animals before mating for signs of this disease and do not use if infected.

DISEASE/CONDITION	SIGNS	CAUSE	TREATMENT	PREVENTION
METRITIS	Low conception rate – small litter size – abortion. Does that fail to lactate 3-5 days after kindling.	Any type of bacterial infections. Often a result of a retained placenta or foeti. Often associated with herd that has increased incidence of 'snuffles'.	Use of an organism susceptible antibiotic in conjunction with injected hormone therapy.	Routine injection of antibiotic and hormone post-kindling.
PNEUMONIA	Difficulty in breathing. Bluish colour to lips, tongue, and ears. Necropsy: inflamed lungs.	Any type of bacterial or virus invasion of respiratory system. Usually at times of stress and often the final stage of 'snuffles'.	Broad spectrum antibiotic. Isolation, eliminate stress.	Assure adequate ventilation. Minimise stress.
LISTERIOSIS	Sudden death, abortion, failure to eat, weight loss. On necropsy, grey-white spots on liver, spleen, inflamed uterus in pregnant animals.	Listeria sp.	Diagnosis usually made on post-mortem necropsy.	Isolation – good sanitation.
SALMONELLOSIS	Pasty diarrhoea, mainly in young rabbits, high temperature, coma usually precedes death.	Salmonella sp. bacteria.	Isolation, seek professional consultation to treat bacteria susceptible to a prescribed antibiotic.	Good disease control techniques. Isolation of herd. No visitors in rabbitry.
FOOT ABSCESSES	Small nodular abscesses on the feet, legs and toes of infected rabbits. Initially a small number of animals infected that increases in incidence with time.	Infection and irritation of bruised area with Staphlycoccus sp.	Soak infected feet in an iodine solution every 3-4 days. Open abscesses, if necessary.	Strict sanitation.

Disease/Condition	Symptoms	Cause	Treatment	Prevention/Control
PASTEURELLOSIS (expresses itself in several forms) 1. 'Snuffles' (chronic)	Persistent 'sneezing' with a productive nasal discharge that is thin or thick and white in nature. Precursor to many other conditions. Decreased growth rate and production. Primarily an upper respiratory infection where pneumonia is often a secondary complication. Death associated with secondary infection.	*Pasteurella* sp. organism infection associated with stress factors. *Pasteurella* sp. and/or *Bordetella bronchi-septicum*.	No specific treatment with medications successful. Improve ventilation of rabbitry. Administration of antibiotic to prevent secondary infection. Reduce stress factors.	Excellent ventilation, strict culling, development of resistant animal. Minimise stress factors. Isolate sick animals. Chlorinate drinking water.
2. Haemorrhagic septicemia	More acute than 'Snuffles', seen in fryer rabbits most commonly. Pot-bellied, diarrhoea, respiratory distress – often confused with enteritis.	Same as 'Snuffles'.	No specific treatment. Broad spectrum antibiotic to prevent secondary bacterial infection.	Same as above.
3. Abscesses (can also cause the 'Weepy Eye', 'Wry Neck' and several organ inflammations)	Developing 'lumps' anywhere on body – usually around head and shoulders.	Traumatic areas infected with *Pasteurella* sp. organism; or from a *Pasteurella* sp. septicaemia, oftentimes it may take an extended period of time to develop.	Cull from herd. If treated one should drain 'pus' from abcess with a large incision and drain daily. Use a broad spectrum injectible antibiotics for 3-5 days.	Excellent sanitation practices. Early removal of nest box (14-16 days). Improve nest box hygiene.
SORE EYES-NEST BOX	Eyelids stuck shut and eyes fail to open at 10 days. Area beneath lids filled with white 'pus'.	Many types of bacterial conjunctivitis that are usually contracted in the nest box.	Gently open eye and clean pus from area. Instill neomycin ophthalmic 2-3 times per day for 3-5 days.	Strict nest box disinfection. Removal of nest at 12-16 days after kindling.

DISEASE/CONDITION	SIGNS	CAUSE	TREATMENT	PREVENTION
ENTERITIS COMPLEX	Pot-bellied, sits with feet in water, diarrhoea and death.	Varied – will discuss in the specific enteric diseases.	Reduce stress, place on high fibre, bland low energy diet. Can treat with broad-spectrum antibiotic in water to prevent secondary infection.	Keep stress factors at a minimum. Maintain on high fibre diet.
1. Mucoid enteritis	Common in fryer rabbits. 'Jelly'-like secretion in stool, pot-bellied and water-bottle like filled abdominal cavity. Won't eat, grinds teeth and high mortality.	Unknown – caecum impacted, intestinal-tract filled with jelly-like material. Probable cause a combination of factors.	As above.	As above
2. Intestinal coccidia	(See Parasite)			
3. Tyzzer's Disease	Acute diarrhoea, rapid wasting of flesh condition. Death within 1-3 days, most common in 3 week to 8 week old young but can affect all ages. On necropsy small white spots on liver and inflamed caecum.	*Bacillus piliformis* must be differentiated from common enteritis through necropsy findings of small white 'spots' on liver; demonstrating bacteria with specific strain or isolation of organism on embryonating egg.	No specific treatment to date. Some success with tetracycline treatment of the entire herd.	Prevent exposure to the organism through excellent sanitation, herd isolation and rodent control.
4. Enterotoxemia (described by Oregon State University in 1978)	Acute (24 hr) fatal diarrhoea dehydration – on necropsy an enlarged caecum that sometimes has a red discoloration.	Specific bacterium uncertain; but associated closely with high energy feed with low fibre feed content.	Replace pelleted diet with rolled oats and gradually increase the portion of pellets on a daily basis. Treatment with oxytetracycline in drinking water may temporarily correct condition.	Feed diets that are high in fibre (18%) and relatively low in total energy.

ORPHANED KITS (at kindling)	Newborn 'kits' can go up to 72 hrs without nursing as long as they are kept warm and dry. Colostrum milk is of little value in rabbits, and therefore they can be fostered or hand-fed quite easily.	Death of doe at kindling, doe that has kindled more kits than she can adequately nurse.	Does usually nurse the litter only one to two times a day. Place kits on a foster mother. Taking care to touch all kits and there should not be over a 5-day age difference. Feed animals twice daily a substitute formula.	Good management to prevent orphans.
'SCATTERING OF YOUNG AT KINDLING'	Doe fails to make nest for young and scatters on wire or floor. Young die due to exposure.	Poor mothering instinct due to hereditary causes. Rodents or predators in rabbitry. Vitamin A deficiency. Very young does. Incompatible nest.	Fostering the young or feeding the kits as orphans.	Select replacement animals with excellent mothering instinct. Use of subterranean nest boxes. Control predators and rodents in rabbitry. Routine use of water supplemented with vitamins.
EARLY NEST BOX FATALITY	Kits die in nest sometime between second and tenth day.	Agalactia (failure to lactate). Metritis. Fouled nest boxes from urine and faeces. Milk enterotoxemia – doe 'over milks'.	See other entries. Due to habit of doe or improper nest box size. Death so sudden one cannot treat.	Proper kindling management. Proper feeding management at kindling.
SORE HOCKS (Ulcerated foot pads)	Ulcerated area on the bottom of the foot pads that has secondary bacterial infection. Sits on any crock or object that is in the cage. Sits cautiously. Loss of condition, fails to mate and be active.	Small foot pad area for size of body, thin fur covering for pad, nervous animal, long toe nails.	Difficult! Use dry solid surface for animals to rest. Treat ulceration with astringent material on a daily basis until healed.	Selective culling for large, well furred feet. Calm animals. Try not to depend on resting board.

DISEASE/CONDITION	SIGNS	CAUSE	TREATMENT	PREVENTION
MALOCCLUSION 'Buck Teeth', 'Wolf Teeth'	Elongation of upper and/or lower teeth. Oftentimes to the extent that the animal will fail to eat.	Inherited condition in some animals, may be much more complex than originally thought. Breaking of one or more opposing teeth and the tooth elongates without being worn off. Rabbit incisors grow $\frac{1}{2}$ inch or more per month if not worn off.	Cull those animals from herd that have the inherited condition. Clipping teeth can be done; but not an ethical or intelligent practice with inherited malocclusion.	Selective culling to eliminate those defective genes from the herd.
HINDQUARTER PARALYSIS	Rabbit drags rear legs and does not have any (motor control) movement in rear legs. Control of urinary bladder and bowel may be absent. A violent 'scream' from rabbit usually is heard at the time of injury. Can happen during tattooing procedure or may just be present in cage without apparent cause.	Dislocation or fracture of spinal vertebra. Often seen when rabbit struggles or becomes excited and 'thrusts' hind legs backwards.	None – should be humanely euthanized.	Proper handling techniques.
HUTCH BURN (Urine burn) (Often confused with Vent Disease)	'Chapped' or 'galded' area around external genitals and the inside of hind legs. Secondary bacterial invasion common that causes the area to become infected.	Dirty, wet hutches or urine guard that splashes the urine back on the rabbit at times of urination.	Correct cause. Apply antibiotic cream to infected and 'burned' areas.	Strict sanitation. Close attention to the angle of urine guards.
MOON EYE 'Wall Eye'	Glazed or cloudiness to pupil or cornea of eye. Pupil slow to respond to light stimulus.	Increased pressure within the eye globe due to genetic defect.	None – hereditary defect.	Eliminate animals that carry this genetic defect from the herd.

146

Condition	Symptoms	Cause	Treatment	Prevention
CAKED BREAST	Swollen, hard, painful and milk filled breast. Usually occurs just after kindling, just after weaning or after death of litter. Often a precursor of mastitis.	Engorgement of mammary gland with milk in response to the feed intake in comparison to the milk consumed by the young.	Withhold all concentrates for 72 hr. Give only roughage and water. 'Strip' milk from teats, if necessary.	Monitor feed consumption. Withhold feed prior to kindling, at weaning and upon death of litter.
HEAT PROSTRATION	Increased respiratory rate. Wet around the mouth that may be blood tinged. Holding head high and blue tinge to ears and mouth. Prostration and death.	High temperature. Usually accompanied by high humidity. Animals sitting directly in sunlight without air movement.	Remove animal to cool place. If completely prostrate, submerge in cool water.	Keep air moving around the animals. Use of plastic bottles filled with water that is frozen solid.
'SCABBY' NOSE	Scabs around nose and mouth. May contain a white-yellow discharge.	Usually found in animals with severe lesions of vent disease or hutch burn. Contracted through the normal coprophagy (eating night faeces).	Prevent vent disease and hutch burn. Treat cause and apply antibiotic ointment to lesions on nose.	Decrease activities in rabbitry. Feed, breed and move at night when temperature is lowest.
COPROPHAGY (eating of night faeces)	Usually seen at night or early morning where animal will consume the fecal material (soft) directly from the rectum.	Normal.	Don't want to disrupt.	None. The rabbit's way of increasing the absorption of some nutrients of the diet.
NON-SPECIFIC DIARRHOEA (not related to bacteria or nutrition)	Profuse diarrhoea following the treatment with antibiotics of some other non-enteric condition, fails to eat and death with 24-48 hrs.	Alteration of normal bacteria flora of intestinal tract. Allows for 'over growth' of certain types of bacteria and alteration of the acidity (pH) of digestive tract and this results in severe diarrhoea.	Discontinue antibiotics, reinoculate gastrointestinal tract with 'healthy' bacteria.	Use antibiotic only when needed and the proper dosage.

DISEASE/CONDITION	SIGNS	CAUSE	TREATMENT	PREVENTION
		VIRAL DISEASES		
PAPILLOMATOSIS (warts about nose and mouth)	Small benign tumors in mouth or around mouth.	Virus	Cull	Isolation of herd.
INFECTIOUS MYXOMATOSIS †	Primarily seen in coastal areas of California and Oregon during May to August. Severe conjunctivitis, fails to eat, high temperature, inflamed and edematosis genitals and ears, respiratory infection in later stages and death.	Virus – transmitted by mosquitoes.	Depopulate herd, burn and bury affected animals. Seek professional assistance.	Mosquito control, control the brush rabbit.
		PARASITIC CONDITIONS		
EXTERNAL PARASITES 1. 'Warbles'	Swelling or isolated 'lump' around the neck or shoulders. Must be differentiated from abscess.	Botfly *Cuterebra* sp.	Enlarge breathing pore and remove the parasite using care not to traumatise the parasite as it may cause acute death due to shock. After removal – daily application of an antiseptic cream.	Control flies in rabbitry though screening or keeping the rabbitry in a darkened condition.
2. Ringworm	Loss of hair in circular fashion with 'sore' in the middle. Most common on feet and legs of young rabbits, but can be seen in adults and on any location of body.	Fungus – contagious to human beings and caution should be used in handling rabbits with this condition.	Individual animals should be treated with daily application of iodine to affected area. If a herd problem exists, professional consultation should be sought concerning the addition of griseofulvin to the feed for extended periods of time.	Herd isolation, disinfection of cages and equipment. Rodent and predator control.

3. Fur Mite	Loss of fur around face, neck and back.	Fur mites – *Cheyletiella parasitovora, Listraphorcy gibus*.	Application of cat flea powder. Repeat 10 days after initial treatment to insure total control of life cycle.	Herd isolation, good sanitation, selective bedding materials. Rodent control.
4. Mange Mite Infestation	Scratch frequently – often inflicting self trauma. Loss of hair on chin, head, base of ears and neck.	Mange mite – *Sarcoptes scabiei* or *Notocdres cati*.	Seek professional consultation. Treat with 7.5% chloroform and 0.12% rotenone or 0.5% malathion containing dust.	Isolation of herd. Excellent rodent control. Selective bedding.
5. Ear Mites (Ear Canker)	Shaking head, scratching at ears, 'scabby' formation inside ear due to accumulation of serum and blood, secondary bacterial infection.	Infestation of inside outer ear with mite. *Psoroptes cuniculi*.	Daily placement of oil in ear for 3 days, repeating treatment at 10 day intervals will be effective in suffocation of mites. Addition of parasiticide, such as Malthine or rotenone will increase the effectiveness of the treatment.	Isolation of herd. Medication placed in ears of every rabbit in herd once a month will rid the rabbitry of the parasite.
Pin Worms	Failure of signs unless overwhelming infestation. Slow growth rate, poor condition, decrease in resistance to other enteric diseases. Difficulty in getting rabbits in fur condition.	Pin Worm – *Passalurus ambiguus*	Use of a wormer. Seek professional advice. Phenothiozine feed (1gm/50 mg feed). Newer wormers effective; but not approved by USDA for use in rabbits.	Sanitation and periodic use of 'wormer'.
Tapeworm Larva	No visible signs. Rabbit is the intermediate host for 2 tapeworms in dogs and 1 in cats. On necropsy, a cyst may be found in the viscera, under the skin, or in the liver.	Dogs – *Taenia pisiformis* and *Taenia serialis*; Cats – *Taenia taeniaeformis*	Seen only on necropsy or during processing.	Do not allow dogs and cats in the rabbitry at a place the rabbit feed can be contaminated. Do not feed viscera to dogs and cats.

149

DISEASE/CONDITION	SIGNS	CAUSE	TREATMENT	PREVENTION
Whipworms	Infestation rarely a problem. Poor growth rate, rough hair coat, increased incidence of diarrhoea that contains 'flecks' of blood.	*Trichuris* sp.	Seek professional advice.	Strict sanitation. Isolation of rabbitry from pets, rodents and predators.
Abnormal parasite larva migration in the central nervous system.	None, to partial or complete paralysis.	Protozoan parasite – *Encephalitozoon cuniculi*	None	Control urine contamination in the rabbitry.
INTERNAL PARASITES Coccidiosis (2 forms)	May be precursor to other enteric diseases.	Protozoan parasite.	Treatment same for both forms of coccidiosis.	
1. Intestinal Form (low infestation common)	Diarrhoea, low rate of gain, poor fur and flesh condition, pot-bellied – lower resistance and produces stress for other secondary infections. Does not cause liver pathology on necropsy.	Several species of the genus *Eimeria*.	Use of coccidiocide on a regular basis being sure the life cycle is controlled. Depending on medication the animal should be treated for 10 consecutive or treat 5 days, off medication 5 to 10 days and treat again for 5 days. Medicated drinking water treatment appears to be most successful; however feed additives can be used. Use of coccidiocides should be rotated for best results. Sulfaquinoxaline has been drug of choice at 0.04% in drinking water. Newer coccidiocide, amprolium, and such are effective; but have not been approved by USDA for use in rabbits.	Excellent sanitation, self-cleaning hutches, automatic waterer and feeders, wire brushing of wire floor routinely. Prevent faecal contamination. The use of coccidiocides every 3-4 months.
2. Hepatic Form	Diarrhoea, poor fur and flesh condition, lowers resistance to other disease as stress on animal. On necropsy, large white spots on liver.	Coccidia – *Eimeria steidae*		Same as above.

150

WET DEWLAP	Wet fur on the dewlap with a changing colour of the skin to green or dark colour. A gangrenous odour often associated with this condition.	Dragging dewlap, large pendulous fold of skin beneath the chin, in water crock. Especially in summer. This causes matting of fur and secondary bacterial infection that oftentimes turns skin green and becomes very odouriferous.	Clip the wet fur from the infected area and apply antibiotic ointment or cream to the infected area.	Raise water crocks off floor 3-4in. Use water bottles or automatic waterers. Place light bulb or rubber ball in crock so animal will drink at edge of crock.
WRY NECK TORTICOLLIS (otitis media)	Turning of the head to one side, loss of balance, continuous roll when excited. Usually does not interfere with the appetite of the animal until later stages of the disease.	Inflammation of the middle ear, the balance mechanism of the body. The bacteria usually isolated is a Pasteurella sp. Often associated with the extension of upper respiratory infections.	Very difficult. Daily instillation of tetracycline ointment as otic drops, about 60% successful. Usually not associated with ear canker.	Proper ventilation. Keep incidence of respiratory infections to a minimum.
'SLOBBERS'	Rabbit salivates profusely and face, chin and dewlap area become very moist or wet.	Abscessed tooth, feeding of excessive amount of 'green' feed that has been sprayed with certain insecticides or pesticides.	Correct tooth condition. Remove green feed from the diet.	Feed dry ration. Avoid feed that has had chemical treatment.
CANNIBALISM (during or after kindling)	Appendages may be missing or entire carcass consumed except the head. Most common in first litter does.	Inherent nervousness. Mishap of consuming appendages while assisting with mouth during kindling process. Presence of predators or rodents in kindling area. Does deprived of sufficient water.	Provide ideal kindling conditions.	Select does with good mothering instincts. Restrict rodents and predators from kindling area.

DISEASE/CONDITION	SIGNS	CAUSE	TREATMENT	PREVENTION
FUR CHEWING	Chewing of fur on body or other body parts. Fur can be chewed by self or other animals in pen.	Low fibre diet; boredom, vice, developing enteritis.	Increase fibre in diet by feeding hay or straw; remove individual chewing fur from pen. Addition of 5 lb of magnesium oxide per ton of feed 'sometimes' will stop fur chewing.	High fibre ration. Addition of magnesium oxide to regular ration.
HAIR BLOCKAGE 'Fur Ball' or 'Fur Block'	Intermittent diarrhoea, poor appetite or periods of no appetite, loss of weight, moult, pulling fur, appearance of above sign in only one animal in herd.	Physical blockage of small intestines that will not allow ingested food to flow through the intestinal tract.	Daily dosing animal with ½ tsp of mineral oil for 3 consecutive days. Repeat once a week.	Daily feeding roughage to animals prone to this condition (Angora, kindling does, etc.). Periodic (weekly) administration of small amount of vaseline or mineral oil to animals susceptible to this condition.
CANNIBALISM (during growing stage)	Chewing on each other while caged together. Sometimes to the extent to cause death.	Overcrowding; sexually mature males in growing cages; lack of adequate drinking water.	Relieve overcrowding. Castration of male animals. Fresh water at all times.	Cage growing rabbits that mature early and gain at a slower rate individually. Supply fresh water.
KETOSIS (Pregnancy toxemia)	Sudden death of doe just prior to or just after kindling. Death usually so sudden that there are not any other signs manifested. Upon necropsy a large 'yellow-red' liver.	Usually seen in does that are excessively fat and when body called upon to break down the fat suddenly this condition occurs due to the end products of fat metabolism – ketones.	No specific treatment due to the acuteness of the disease. Seek professional assistance to administrate 50% dextrose parenterally.	Do not let replacement does get excessively fat.
DYSTOCIA (difficult kindling)	The doe will sit in nest box for long periods of time, straining, 'bloodmessed' nest. One or more of litter with appendages (ears, legs) missing or	Small doe of the varieties with large heads (Netherlands Dwarf, Holland Lop); mal-presentation of young at delivery.	If 'kit' in birth canal, inject with 0.25 cc – ½ cc oxytocin USP. Danger of rupturing uterus of does exists.	Do not let doe get excessively fat. Allow doe to be mature before mating.

Condition	Signs	Cause	Treatment	Prevention
'YOUNG DOE DEATH SYNDROME'	Does that suddenly die 1-2 weeks after kindling. Usually in first litter does but can be in older ones. Other signs inconsistent.	Metritis caused by *Staphylococcus* sp. This type may be more chronic and show more signs than with enterotoxemia. Enterotoxemia (most common) death due to a toxin produced in digestive tract similar to enterotoxemia in enteritis in fryer rabbits.	Normally too sudden onset to treat. If mastitis present, treat with antibiotics.	Restrict feed 24-48 hrs prior to kindling and increase total feed intake after kindling until 5-7 days post-kindling.
AGLACTIA (failure to milk)	The kits dehydrate, fur becomes rough, listlessness and death. This can happen anytime during the first 3 weeks of the kit's life.	Doe fails to milk; common at kindling time, especially in first litter does due to hereditary instincts. Also occurs at 7-10 days due to post-kindling uterus infection and 2-3 weeks due to insufficient caloric intake or mastitis.	Treatment of doe with oxytocin to stimulate milk production. Treatment of doe with antibiotics and hormones. Adequate caloric intake.	Routine post-kindling (within 24 hrs) injection of oxytocin USP. Select breeding stock that has ability to lactate readily. Routine post-kindling injection with hormone and antibiotics.
'RED URINE'	Red discoloured urine that does not contain 'blood clots'. Most commonly seen in snow-covered areas that makes condition more noticeable.	Normal – there is not any pathology involved. Due to incomplete metabolism of food nutrients in some animals.	None	More common on high legume hay-contained diets.
'FETAL GIANTISM'	Difficult birth (dystocia) of an extremely large fetus. Does 3-4 days late in kindling. Sits in nest. Abnormal straining and a 'bloody' discharge from the vulva.	Usually exists in does with very small (1-2) litter size. Tendency to go over the normal gestation time. Usually present in does that are excessively heavy (fat).	C-section. Costly and not practical unless very expensive breeding stock. Use of oxytocin may rupture uterus. Manual assistance in delivery if a part of the foetus is presented. Seek professional help.	Do not allow does to become excessively fat. Select does that have good sized litters.

APPENDIX II

ADDRESSES OF NATIONAL BODIES OF THE RABBIT FANCY
American Rabbit Breeders Association Inc.
1925 S. Main
Box 426
Bloomington
Illinois 61701
USA

British Rabbit Council
Purefoy House
7 Kirkgate
Newark
Nottinghamshire
UK

Rabbit Council of New Zealand Inc
PO Box 1633
Auckland
New Zealand

BIBLIOGRAPHY

Aitken, F.C. & Wilson, W.K. (1962), *Rabbit Feeding for Meat and Fur*, Commonwealth Agricultural Bureau. 2nd edition.

American Rabbit Breeders Association Inc (1984), *A Progressive Program for Raising Better Rabbits and Cavies.*

British Rabbit Council (1981), *Breed Standards*, B.R.C. Newark UK.

British Rabbit Council (1986), *Breed Standards*, B.R.C. Newark UK.

Department of the Environment (1985), *Planning Permission: A Guide to Householders.*

Castle, W.E. (1940), *Mammalian Genetics*, Cambridge, Mass.

Cheek, P. & Paton, L. (1982). *Rabbit Production*, Interstate, 5th edition.

Lang, J. (1981), 'Nutrition of the commercial rabbit', *Nutr. Abstr. Rev.* **51**: 197–225, 287–302.

Rabbit Council of New Zealand Inc. (1984), *Standards of Perfection.*

Robinson, R. (1958), 'Genetics of the rabbit', *Bibliogr. Genet.*, **17**: 229–558.

Sandford, J.C. (1979), *The Domestic Rabbit*, Crosby & Lockwood, Staples Granada Publishing 3rd edition.

Swain, P.B. (1955) *Recent Genetics of the Domestic Rabbit*, Advance. Genet., 7, 183–226.

Glossary

Adult The age at which an animal reaches sexual maturity, or when the breed standard allows for it to be shown with fully developed rabbits.

Agouti A South American mammal whose name is used to describe the three-band markings and shades of several other animals, including the rabbit, that have a similar appearance.

Agouti Self A black rabbit with some Agouti hairs, especially around the haunches.

Allele One of a series of mutant genes which can occupy the same position on the chromosome.

Any Age A show class in which rabbits of all ages may compete equally.

Back The part of the body from the base of the skull to the tail.

Balance The overall impression of the rabbit, the relationship of the parts of the body to each other.

Barred Lines of a different colour, e.g. white, on the feet of darker-coloured rabbits.

Belly Generally the underpart of the body from the chest to the tip of the tail.

Blaze The white marking in the Dutch rabbit that extends from the nostrils to the base of the ears.

Bow Leg Where the front legs of the rabbit bend outwards in 'Queen Anne' style.

Breed A rabbit or a collection of different-coloured rabbits possessing the same body type, fur type or other distinguishing characteristics.

Brindling Two different-coloured hairs interspersed together, as in the intermediate portion of the Fox.

Broken Term used to describe the pattern of the two-tone rabbit of the Lop or other breeds that contain the heterozygous system for English spotting.

Buck A male rabbit.

Buck Teeth Where the two front incisors protrude beyond the level of the other teeth.

Butterfly The butterfly-shaped marking on the nose of breeds which carry the genes for English spotting.

Carriage The stance of the rabbit, the way in which it displays itself.

Centromere The point on which the chromosomes pivot during the production of new cells.

Chain Markings   The colour spotting running down the sides of the English rabbit.

Charlie   In English rabbits, the homozygous *EnEn* in which the rabbit contains far more white than in the exhibition English rabbit.

Chest   The part of the body from the throat to the belly.

Cheek   The skin covering the sides of the upper jaw; the near-circular markings of the Dutch rabbit found in that position.

Chromatid   One of the two identical parts into which the chromosome divides during reproduction.

Chromosome   The strands of hereditary material in the nucleus of the cell.

Cobby   Short-coupled animal with well-rounded hindquarters.

Condition   The overall state of health, nutrition, cleanliness and moult of the rabbit.

Definition   The clarity of separation of the three bands of the Agouti pattern.

Density   The number of hairs per centimetre of skin.

Dewlap   The flap of loose skin found on the neck of some animals. Allowable in some breeds of rabbit but not others. Because of their larger size, does are more likely to have dewlaps than bucks.

Diploid Pairs   The complementary pair of genes occurring in the same position on the chromosome, donated by the buck and doe.

Disqualification   A feature which is so bad that any prize which might have been awarded should be withheld, as opposed to a fault for which points are merely deducted. The presence of faults does not necessarily preclude a rabbit from winning a prize.

Doe   A female rabbit.

Dominant   A gene whose characteristic will mask that of its diploid partner should that be recessive.

Fine Coat   A coat which lacks resistance, due mainly to a lack of primary guard hairs or the presence of thinner hair shafts.

Finish   The overall appearance of the animal. A good finish is the sparkle or lustre that is the hallmark of a champion.

Flabby   An animal in which the skin fits loosely. The result of loss of weight, a fault of condition.

Flat Coat   A coat in which the fur lies close to the skin.

Fly-Back Coat   A coat which, when stroked in the wrong direction, rapidly returns to its original postion.

Gene   The individual unit of inheritance.

Genotype   The actual genetic make-up of the individual as opposed to its physical appearance.

Gestation Period   The time during which the embryos develop, the period from fertilisation to parturition.

Guard Hairs   The longer thicker hairs of the pelt.

Herring Bone   The coloured markings running along the saddle from the neck to the tail in the English rabbit. It should be unbroken.

Heterozygous Where two genes of the diploid pair are different.

Homozygous Where the two genes of the diploid pair are indentical.

Intermediate Coat The coat at a stage between that of the kitten and the full adult.

Intensifiers Hereditary factors which increase or decrease the effect of colour or other inherited characteristics.

Kindle To give birth.

Kittens The young, particularly the very young, of the rabbit.

Lacing The small area of self-coloured hairs at the tip of the ears in any rabbit carrying the Agouti gene.

Lactation The secretion of milk for the young.

Locus A particular gene position on the chromosome.

Lop Any breed with enlarged ears which flop rather than stand erect.

Mal-occlusion A defect in the meeting of the upper and lower teeth when the jaws are brought together.

Mandolin The curved shape of the back seen in certain breeds which resembles a mandolin in shape.

Mealy Yellowish meal-coloured areas which appear as a fault in some red-brown breeds.

Meiosis The formation of reproductive cells.

Mitosis The formation of non-reproductive cells.

Mutation An alternative feature to that most commonly found in the wild rabbit, the animal displaying such a feature.

Normal Any feature, such as size, fur type or colour, found in the wild rabbit.

Paunch The soft part of the belly from the ribcage to just in front of the hind legs.

Pea Spot A mark in front of each ear found in Tan pattern rabbits.

Pearl The white-coloured middle band of the Chinchilla pattern.

Pelt The skin and fur of the rabbit (noun); the action of removing the pelt (verb).

Phenotype The actual appearance of the animal as opposed to the genotype, which is the genetic composition.

Primaries The primary guard hairs, the longest and thickest of all hairs occupying their own follicle.

Primary Follicle The opening in the skin from which the primary guard hair grows. These are fewer in number than the secondary follicles and their presence provides the coat with resistance.

Racy Fine athletic body, a virtue in Belgian Hares and Checkered Giants, a fault in most other breeds.

Roll-Back A coat which slowly regains its original position after being stroked in the wrong direction.

Saddle The back of the rabbit; the position of the colour separation in the Dutch rabbit.

Sandy   The colour of sand found in some breeds, often due to the presence of the wide-band gene.

Scut   The tail of the rabbit.

Secondaries   Secondary guard hairs, shorter than primaries.

Secondary Follicle   The opening from which both the secondary guard hairs and the fur fabric issue.

Self   Any single-coloured rabbit; a mutation of the Agouti series. In the English rabbit, the result of the *enen* gene pair in which the rabbit contains extra colour.

Siblings   Full brothers and sisters, although not necessarily from the same litter.

Silver   The accumulation of white hairs evenly distributed throughout a coloured background.

Smellers   The long whiskers growing from the upper lip.

Smut   The butterfly markings found on the nose of breeds carrying genes for English spotting.

Stops   The white markings on the lower hind legs of the Dutch rabbit.

Symmetry   The comparability of two sides of the animal, e.g.the absolutely identical chain markings on the sides of the English rabbit.

Table (Box) Show   A show in which the rabbits are not put on display but remain in their boxes when not required for judging.

Texture   A term applied to the feel of the coat, whether soft or coarse.

Ticking   A small number of hairs of a second colour distributed amongst the main colour, e.g. on the sides of the Tans.

Tucked Up   When a rabbit displays itself in such a way that it appears to be short-coupled, with the body hunched up.

Type   The overall shape, balance and conformation of the body.

Variety   One or more of the distinct colours in which it is possible to obtain a breed.

Wall Eyes   Where the eyes are all or partly of a different colour from that required by the breed, e.g. blue instead of brown eyes in the Dutch rabbit.

Wool   The fur of Angora breeds.

INDEX

DATE DUE